leading with love

A NURSE'S STORY

Connie White Delaney
Professor & Dean of Nursing
University of Minnesota

Shelagh Klein

Contact Information

Publisher:
Educated Change LLC
Amplify Purpose and Build Community

educatedc.com
LWL@educatedc.com

Illustration by Zoé du Toit
Design by Ursula van Graan
Lindy Augustyn

For more information or to order copies:
conniedelaney.com

We shall not cease from exploration, and the end of all our exploring will be to arrive where we started and know the place for the first time.

T.S. Eliot

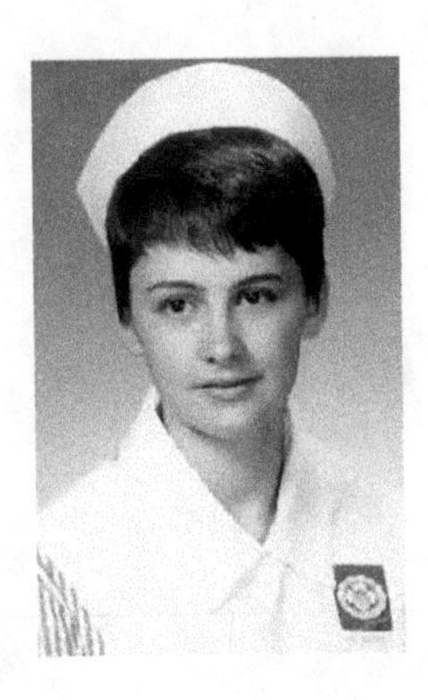

Table of Contents

Acknowledgments

> "There is always a light, if only we're brave enough to see it, if only we're brave enough to be it."
>
> Amanda Gorman

I celebrate with deepest gratitude the life that I have been given. My family celebrates those who came before and anticipates and dreams of those yet to come, by birth and association. We weave the tapestry with experiences and lenses anchored in my parents Edmond N and Betty JoAnn White. I am thankful for each of my siblings—Sue, E. Clark and husband Christopher, Craig, Lora and husband Randy, Loren and wife Wendy and Ann—and the diversity and yet common threads we weave.

My son Jeremy Andrews, his wife Jessica O'Mara, and their four daughters, Ashley, Aana, Skye, and Storme, and their budding families bring steady discoveries. We ride the waves of change and transformation together, with unwavering inclusivity.

We all have light, a book, and a story inside. I thank Peter Klein for the first words of encouragement. The lived experiences of the Educated Change team and Anne Pryor helped make all this possible while I focused on the School of Nursing during the changes forced on us. Shelagh arrived inside my heart, head, and soul to deliver the written expressions for which I had no words.

I am grateful to the faculty, staff, students, alumni, and partners at the University of Minnesota School of Nursing and our continuous journey of discovery, for co-creating a culture of abundance, transparency, flowing in purpose, and welcoming me to be "one of us." A special thank you to Director of

Communications and Marketing Steve Rudolph, the Board of Visitors, and alumni. Patricia Robertson, thanks for those early insights, edits, and questions.

Deep family stories, lived and heard as they are handed down from generation to generation, coupled and integrated with my professional family from across the globe. Each of you has given me the lived experiences of the action of love. I thank each of you. You are the "light in form" of this book. I am grateful for Bill Torvund, who shared the expansiveness of this experience we call life and welcomed and advanced the synergy of perceived separation into Oneness.

And I am grateful for You. For your curiosity, and, most of all, for your willingness to read, integrate, and generate love and questions of expansion and transformation. I am grateful for your willingness to think beyond the I Am and discover the ultimate... We Are.

Introduction

We have a nursing shortage. It is well documented and growing throughout the United States and the world. And so we put up posters and print flyers and shout out: We Need You Now"!

Notice this shortage emphasizes "nursing", and nursing care, leadership, education, and service. Yes, "nursing" is a verb, not a noun; it is relationship and action in partnership with individuals, families, communities, and organizations—nurses nursing. In order to address this desperate call, we have to revolutionize how we lead. Change the way we relate with our family, friends, neighbors, employees, students, and potential nurses. Change the way we relate to ourselves, the person on the street corner, or any intelligence. We need to "lead with love."

Do you know and care about the people you work with? Do you know what inspires them? Are you intentional when working with yourself? With others? Are you focused on only succeeding yourself, or do you lead in a manner that inspires others, helps them further their purpose, and fosters their growth? I strive to be anchored in purpose and essence, rather than the kind of leader who stands on the top of the ladder and pushes others down or off. Now with many years of experience, I have learned to help people advance; and I've learned to do it with love. I believe in leading with love.

And I pause to reflect on "leading with love." While our cultures immerse us in romantic attraction, idealization, and emotional love, "leading with love" is a leadership practice. Like nursing, Leading With Love is a verb, action, and a way of living. It is a practice anchored in essence, purpose, and intentionality that transcends self. "Leading with Love" is about connection beyond self and meaning beyond one's self. Some call this soulness, soul-filled. While it is about being and sharing beyond self, it is also about Oneness. It is a practice anchored in consciousness and intentionality, and strength of compassion, respect, truth, and transparency. It is about the I Am, thus the We Are.

And because we are looking to the future, we need to incorporate the new kid on the block. Artificial Intelligence. When I started my nursing education, I combined my learning with mathematics and continued by gaining expertise in informatics. We can't imagine nursing today without the data that we now use to diagnose, treat, and heal our patients. And now it is artificial intelligence. The speed with which this tool can help us, the accuracy of the endless data available, and the volume of information are endless. AI will be the new nursing assistant. AI is not an entity on its own; it is a key to a better healthcare future, and it is also a risk to humanity's existence. If we want a human outcome for AI, we need to lead with love. This is not a suggestion, this is necessary. Great things can be used or abused. We need to engage AI and use it to the benefit of all things, or it will use us and possibly destroy us. We need AI in the base data of the LLM (Large Language Model). Visit conniedelaney.com for more information on how you can help keep our future and AI safe.

In this book, I invite you to hear and feel some of my personal and professional experiences, some that are deeply painful and some filled with joy. I invite you to discover what I have learned, and what I have to share. My hope is these stories will awaken the stories and book within you, the deep peace and purpose. Perhaps it will invite you to say "yes" to being here, in knowing this place and time, knowing and celebrating you in the NOW.

I, Connie the nurse, can transform health care and co-create a new world. I can, We can—as a team. Everything I am is a product of something much bigger. It is WE who are changing the world, and it is WE who will lead with love and encourage more people to become nurses in all parts of their life—who transform and lead with love by nursing our world and all intelligence around us. There is a higher purpose beyond myself in this world, and my aim is to be a part of that purpose, part of the solution, part of the love. I wish that in reading my stories, you find hope and commit in your life to leading with love. When you have your stories, please share them with me Connie@conniedelaney.com

I Am, We Are
Connie

I Was Born to Be Invisible

I had no great dreams or high ambitions. I wasn't interested in fame or fortune. I wasn't set on curing cancer or jetting into outer space. I didn't set myself apart. I always felt that I was part of something bigger. I was meant to be here in this world, part of the big picture; not the big picture myself.

And that has made all the difference.

"We've found your husband's car," said the sheriff. Shyly I asked what he meant. "It's best to come and see."

I sat frozen as my father drove the familiar road. Trees stood naked and lonely as the long road stretched into the woods. The gravel chafed with the tires as my heart chafed with my soul. The repetitiveness of the long straight road, the platoon of orderly trees, and the erect, solemn composure of my father added to my unrest. It was twenty miles, yet it seemed two hundred. Although it was a flat road, the ups and downs in my head made me want to vomit. My husband is missing. My husband is missing. My husband is missing.

I'm twenty-five years old. I'm not yet finished with school. I have a four-year-old little boy. I don't know what I'm doing. I'm scared. I'm hurting. I'm so afraid of what I'll find and even more afraid of what I won't find.

The road stretches on. And on and on. The sun is setting, and instead of the jubilation of the last light filtering through the landscape, I feel the loss of the light, the loss of my place in the world, the loss of myself.

And then we see the car. It's hanging on to the shoulder like an old drunk sleeping outside a bar. I remember when we got the car, not any car, a Mercury Cougar. I was elated. It was red and bright and shiny, and now it was dull and dirty, and the sight of it frightened me.

We were slow getting out of our car and walked with trepidation toward the abandoned vehicle. Seeing the inside of the car filled me with horror. I shook and I keeled over sobbing. I wanted to run away and yet I was held with my father's gaze. His loving yet stoic presence held me closely. I'd always depended on my father and he was here when I needed him. Blood was encrusted on the door handles, smeared on the dashboard and dried puddles sat in the dip of the seat. Craig's driver's license, identification papers, and debris were strewn about the car. It was the last chapter in a book I hadn't written. What had happened here and where was Craig?

The search was taken up by the sheriff and the community. Dogs were given Craig's scent, and neighbors, community leaders, and law enforcement from Iowa, Minnesota, and Wisconsin were in on the hunt, searching the mosquito- and rattlesnake-infested deep wooded areas of rural Iowa and neighboring Wisconsin. Nothing. Not a clue was found, and after a month of no leads, the sheriff came to tell us that they were no longer aggressively pursuing the case. As the sheriff walked away he turned, took off his hat and said, "Actually, ma'am, we don't believe Craig is dead."

My father hired a private investigator who pursued the search for months, eventually tracking Craig to northern California. He had left with a woman I thought was a passing whim. Craig had chosen her over me. He had chosen a fake death over divorce. And he had chosen abandonment and self-indulgence over family and the potential growth in our future.

What does this do to one's self-esteem? What hope can there be for a future as a single, partly educated, rejected nobody? I was no longer invisible; I didn't like what I saw.

This is what we often call a tipping point. Does one tip into the sea and drown? Does one give up and take what's been given? Or does one re-emerge? Redefine. Re-examine and release one's self to something bigger. It was this junction in my road, of having lost all faith in religion, ethics, and hard work, that forced me to change. It forced growth and paved a road I hadn't yet dreamed of.

I am. I am. I am.

EDUCATION

I always planned to go to college, and I also wanted to return home to run our family farm. It was a jolt into reality when my dad didn't jump for joy at my reasoning. I knew that I could run the farm and he knew it as well. I had three brothers, and it was a family tradition that they would take over the farm. Thinking, in those days, was limited by convention. Unfortunately, it often still is. This is the way it always has been, and so it shall be. This was a boundary I hadn't thought about, and it shocked me into the actuality that exists for women's rights and opportunities. Despite my hard work and knowledge, it was my gender that would keep me from running my family's farm.

I had so looked up to my father. I wanted to be like him. I wanted to run things. To be in charge. To quietly lead. As I lamented this change in plans, I couldn't help thinking of my mother. I hadn't been very close to her. I was a typical teenage girl and didn't really appreciate my mother. I looked out front instead of looking behind the scenes. My mom ran things. She was attentive. She kept the family going. She took charge of my sister Ann, who has Down's syndrome, and guided her into productive adulthood. Ann is an amazing human being and contributor to society. This is largely due to my mother.

My mother didn't do this center stage. She did it quietly. She wasn't demonstrative. She didn't even hug. She didn't shower me with outward affection. She didn't say, "I love you"; it was in her actions. It was her nursing us in her daily life. It was in her prayerful way of being. We talk today about "leaning in." My mother invented this. Embracing challenge and risk in the workplace sounds so "today", yet the women who kept families together, who fed their tribe, who worked in the background to help others shine—this was my mother and so many other women of her age. They are the pillars we stood on to get where we are. It took my young self quite a while to get there, and I am grateful. I stood on my mother's back when I didn't even realize she was there to support me.

And so I continued in college.

Majors and potential career paths were also limited for women. Especially if you're a girl from a rural area in a midwestern state. I loved math and excelled in it in school. Because this was the 60's, my choices for education came down to teaching, nursing, or secretarial work. I chose nursing. I wasn't one of the many who felt "called" to the field or "always wanted to be a nurse." However, my aunt was a nurse at Rochester Methodist Mayo, and her stories intrigued me. She left behind, at my grandparents' home, huge stacks of books. I was drawn to the texts about nursing, health care, and the entire medical system. Grazing through my aunt's academic leftovers added to my hunger. I was drawn to the idea of service. I felt empowered to share myself with others, especially the marginalized.

I was accepted into a three-year diploma nursing program and left home for a hospital-based nursing school a hundred miles away. After a couple of years, I transferred to a four-year baccalaureate program where I could combine my two loves. I declared a double major in nursing and mathematics.

The school administration and mathematics advisor were happy to accommodate my schedule; the nursing program initially questioned whether I knew what I was doing. Did I have a real commitment to nursing? Did I have focus, and was nursing my priority?

I knew that I could learn mathematics and nursing, Like I knew that I could manage a farm, and this time my yearning was realized, and I was given a chance. Surely things were starting to change.

When I arrived for my first mathematics class, I was the only student. The professor said the course would need to be canceled due to low enrollment. The class was not financially viable.

The two sides of my thinking self, the aggressive learner and the docile accepter, undertook this reality calmly as I told the professor it was okay. I had already purchased the book and told him I would study it regardless of the canceled class.

I was shocked. This open-minded, benevolent man listened to me and cared about my aspirations. He could have focused on his schedule, barked out the "class is canceled" announcement and walked out of the room. In that quiet pause, Professor Larry Krajewski suggested we do an independent study. He became my mathematics advisor and helped me navigate the mathematical road toward my future. Encountering angels in one's life is a gift I'm thankful for daily. And the wings this professor gave me I still use to fly today.

Nursing wasn't always an appreciated profession. In the very early days, nurses were not even trained. They were "helpers" who were given the basic jobs of feeding and bathing the patients. They offered comfort, not expertise.

It wasn't until the 19th century and the amazing woman, Florence Nightingale, that modern nursing developed. She founded the first professional nursing school at St Thomas' Hospital in London. It's hard for us to believe today that hygiene was not an original practice in medicine. Florence Nightingale highlighted the importance of hygiene along with nutrition and comfort in healthcare. It was her work during the Crimean war that gained her acknowledgment and garnered support for the profession. Florence Nightingale was a model for women, for healthcare professionals and for the future of nursing. Her accomplishments still remind us today of the importance of making change, challenging the status quo, and bringing a profession like nursing into the modern world.

I was a young single mother who grew up on a farm in the midwestern part of the United States. I knew that I had purpose. And my purpose was evolving. I will be a nurse, I said to myself, and I still am.

EARLY DAYS

It was in my early days, before college, before nursing, and before the guidance of generous professors, that my seeds were planted. Growing up on a farm is like being born into a secret that city folks don't get. It's magical.

I was born and grew up in northeastern Iowa. The nearest town was Waterville, which sits in Paint Creek Township. And painted creeks we had. The streams teamed with fish, and the woods were bountiful. The earth held its riches and my life brimmed with the means provided by my family.

Emily Dickinson wrote a famous poem called "Heaven"—is what I cannot reach:

> "Heaven"—is what I cannot reach!
> The Apple on the Tree—
> Provided it do hopeless—hang—
> That—"Heaven" is—to Me!

In my youth, we memorized things. State flags, capitals, prepositions, and poems. I took this in my stride and enjoyed the poems about nature, however, I could never agree with Emily Dickinson. How could heaven be something she couldn't reach?

I lived in heaven. Whether it was the barefoot days of summer or trudging through winter snow, I did it with gusto. Nature was my nursery. Looking after the cows in the barn with my dad and my brother gave me a feeling of accomplishment, something one only learns through experience. Managing the herd, daily milking, feeding, and keeping up the pastures took hours, and I had plenty of time to talk about the world with my father. This wasn't trickle-down living; this was living from the bottom up. My father never talked down to me; together we discussed significant issues. How we could expand the farm, how to keep the calves healthy, how to prevent mastitis in the milking herd, and the choices we made for crops. We worked towards preserving the farm. We wanted not to grow it into a large conglomerate. We wanted to learn and practice the conservation of the land, feeding the world, and being blessed with the opportunity and the stewardship this gave us. After a morning of milking, we would stand sweating from our chores, and together we looked out upon heaven. We were grateful before I heard about the importance of gratitude; we celebrated life with the exuberance we saw in the sun's rising and setting. I wasn't taught limitations; I was encouraged to dream. I'm sorry, Emily Dickinson, I grew up in heaven, and the apples were delicious.

And it's not only Dickinson who speaks about heaven. Florence Nightingale said that "Mankind must make heaven before we can go to heaven, in this world as in any other." I learned to look at my life as a kind of heaven and I learned that I had to make it. Heaven wasn't going to be handed to me. Whether we are influenced by a parent or a teacher, a writer or a famous nurse, life is what we take from it and what we give to it. Everything is already there; we only have to pick the apple from the tree and eat.

Going forward after my husband's departure, I continued with my degree at Viterbo University St Luke's Hospital and also sat for my Licensed Practical Nursing (LPN) degree license. I could then work for experience and for money to complete a four-year baccalaureate degree in nursing and mathematics. I worked at the Veterans Memorial Hospital in Waukon, Iowa, in labor, nursery and delivery, and at St Francis Hospital in La Crosse, Wisconsin, in intensive care.

Working in intensive care was a monumental influence in my career. I was attracted to this field early on in my interest in nursing. I wanted to help the most vulnerable, the sickest, the ones with the least hope. And hope was what I had to offer. I believed in myself, and I believed in my craft, and I believed in the human body and its healing properties. I was confident in using technology and my newly acquired experience to save lives. I enjoyed the new family I acquired. I had recently learned that family was more than mom and dad. The professionals I worked with on a daily basis became my extended family. We worked in harmony. And harmony is what carries the tune towards recovery.

I became involved with the patients' families. I became the go between—a special opportunity to connect the medical operations with the family's understanding and support of their father or wife or mother or child. It was a privilege to be their guide.

I can remember my very first patient. Lester was from the middle of Iowa. He seemed extremely old to me despite being in his sixties. He was about ten feet tall and his giant farmer's body dwarfed the bed. He wasn't as big or as tall as I thought he was; however, that's the feeling I still hold. He'd had a stroke and he couldn't talk. Being a farm kid myself, I immediately bonded with my gentle giant of a patient. He so wanted to ask me things and tell me things and he cried in his frustration. I didn't need any special courses or degrees to connect with this man. It was one human being relating to another. This very first patient experience solidified my conviction that nursing was to be my life.

Working in this unit not only gave me experience and the funds to take care of myself and my son; it filled me with the joy and responsibility of nursing. It was a catalyst for my ongoing learning, and it inspired a desire to continue. I became a graduate student and received a master's in nursing from The University of Iowa, and then became an assistant professor at Luther College in Decorah, Iowa. I believe that moving oneself forward by starting at the bottom, or I should say, beginning, is an integral part of understanding the system. To be a part of something rather than be perched on top of it. My later life as a dean could only have happened after these important years of learning.

When I chose nursing, I was unaware of the profession's shaky beginnings. In the United States, nursing was a low-paying job that was taken on by women with few options. I was one of these women. I was lucky to be a part of the new emerging science of nursing. Greater emphasis was placed on interdisciplinary collaboration and new specialized programs began in fields dedicated to pediatrics, intensive care, and countless other specialties. Nursing now uses informatics, which is a specialized area focusing on the use of technology and data to improve patients' health. My interest in mathematics helped me to be one of the early pioneers in this new field. Informatics would be part of my future and would be integral in the future of patient outcomes. It was a fairly quick decision that led me into the field of nursing, and it was hours and hours and many years of contemplation, education and experience that took me from the daily position at the bedside of a patient to advanced education, a PhD and the move into academia. I felt that I was on the cusp of new ideas, new technologies and new ways of making nursing more impactful.

I stepped out of the barn in my early childhood years, and I was now stepping away from the bedside. I believed I could continue making a difference. It was another risk. I was now accustomed to the unknown and I was excited to move on.

WHO AM I, AND CAN I CHANGE?

I like using the phrase "I am." I am here for a reason. This is not an ego trip. It does not mean I'm more important than others. It means that I am a unique human being, as is each of us. I am grateful for every step of my life that has led to who I am today. I had parents who loved me. I was part of a large family, my immediate family, and also those who came before us. The rural community and farm where I first learned and experienced community was a solid base from which to grow. These gifts have shaped who I am today.

I am an introvert. I start from silence. I'd rather stand on the side and observe than prance on the stage in the middle. As a child, I was successful and happy in academics. I played trumpet in the band. I worked on the farm. My shyness kept me from stepping out. I didn't even go to a restaurant without my parents until I was a senior in high school.

During my years as a nurse, I enjoyed the one-to-one connection with a patient. While some spent their break time chatting in the cafeteria, I loved meeting individually with patients, families, and both medical and hospital staff. I was happy working alone. I felt efficient, confident, and purposeful. These attributes stayed with me into my early academic career, and I was known as the one who "did it alone." I was content to create and innovate alone, teach in the classroom and clinical settings, and gather and synthesize data on my own. In my initial professor role in a small private college, I worked with a dean who suggested I chair the academic redesign and re-accreditation committees. Naturally, I resisted. She continued to push me, insisting that I would learn to work with people at their pace through committee service. And I did. I learned a lot. I discovered one of the most joyful and growth-filled experiences of my life.

I am, and I can change. I can be me, and also part of the great "we". My dream is to stay in oneness, and this was another step towards this goal.

Changing and growing is not losing oneself; it's expanding. It's transforming, and I've learned to trust my connections, relationships, and colleagues without losing my purpose and essence over time.

The staff and faculty in my current role in the School of Nursing care enough to engage with my natural introversion. They also know I live from my core and grow from thinking out loud and listening to them. "You always seem to have this vision," said one of my colleagues, and by recognizing this and me feeling comfortable sharing my thinking, I grow.

I've learned that the unbelievable and unimaginable happen when I contribute my ideas and welcome honest feedback. While I might have a gift of quickly seeing possibilities, connections, relationships, next steps, and complete trajectories of a situation, the way to lean into those things is engaging with others. When we link to each other, a longer and stronger chain unfolds. I am, yes, and I am also part of a whole—a community, a world of interconnectedness. We are all one. Aren't I lucky that I was able to keep myself and add on? This was yet another example of a superior guiding me toward a brighter light.

When I reflect on our personal and professional growth, I continually remind myself that it's not "them" and "me". It's "we". When moving towards oneness, we expand our capacity. We not only grow tall, we also dance. We create harmony.

Perhaps you've heard the story of the little boy who gets a new baby sister. He begs his parents to let him go into the bedroom to be alone with the baby. They finally agree and stand quietly outside the door listening. "Little baby," says the older brother, "can you tell me what God is like? I'm starting to forget." The boy was trying to remember what it was like to be one with God. One with humanity.

Author Damian Mark Smyth says, "We're One, we've always been One, we'll always be One until we think we are not." Here lies our challenge: we are one and yet we believe we are separate; we have forgotten our Oneness.

I had now moved from a student to an LPN. Then I proceeded on to be a Registered Nurse (RN) and filled myself with the opportunities I was given. Teaching classes filled me with another kind of fulfillment and being pushed into something bigger was another chance for growth. Progression is positive. It is life-giving. And ideally it feeds oneself and also those in one's path.

My dream is to be living in oneness; conscious actions are needed for this. We cannot stop at dreaming; we must act.

MY CHOICE, MY LOVE, MY MISSION

When I entered the professional world of nursing, I was in the midst of a changing trajectory for women. While options had been severely limited when I started my nursing program, things were evolving. Opportunities were expanding and available. I was on the cusp. There was now a preference for a bachelor's degree earned from a college or university rather than a nursing diploma. Learning this, I transferred from the diploma program in Iowa to the collegiate bachelor's program in Wisconsin. My equally strong interest in mathematics in the collegiate program led me to earn a double major in nursing and mathematics.

Little did I know at the time that combining the subjects of nursing, mathematics, and analytics was the emerging pathway to a specialty in informatics. And little could I foresee that this intersection of topics would lead to a sustained, ever-evolving academic career. I was teaching at the University of Iowa when the University of Minnesota inquired about my interest in leading its School of Nursing. In the baccalaureate program I was supported in exploring the faculty/dean role. While I aspired to become a dean someday, nursing opportunities and the innovations in informatics had consumed my focus, time, and transformation. I wasn't looking to become a dean when Minnesota called.

I was very committed to my current work when I politely thanked them for their interest and shared that the timing wasn't right. I was focused on informatics, and that's where I thought I should stay.

They persisted. They asked for a one-hour video interview, which I welcomed. I believed it to be the opportunity to point out again that I was too committed to my current position, and also that I hadn't taken the traditional pathway to a deanship. I wondered why they would want me. Didn't they know that I had so many speeding tickets driving University of Iowa vehicles that I was now banned from driving them?

And I was surprised. Minnesota said they were on a trajectory of wanting bold change. And they wanted it now. They wanted—no, needed—someone with informatics expertise. I finished the interview and was still confident that I had conveyed that I was meant to stay where I was. I would continue to focus on the work at hand.

The search team again surprised me when they called the next day and asked if I would consider coming up for a site visit. While I said okay to a confidential one-day visit, I also wanted to share this interest with my current dean. I arrived for the one-day visit, and within one hour of meeting people at the University of Minnesota I knew that this is where I belong for the next evolution of my career.

Sometimes it takes being an outsider to see what is really available, and possible. A tourist appreciates the sites more than those living locally. And that was me. I saw so many opportunities at the school that I felt giddy. Did they know about these? Was this a secret that I was let in on? It was a community that was bursting. The potential was staggering, and I was humbled that they wanted me to be a part of it. I was in flow.

We proceeded with the formal interview process, and I continued to be thrilled at the prospects of this giant candy store. I landed in an unlikely place. I almost pushed away something extraordinary. By saying yes, I made my life bigger. The Indian Jesuit priest Paul Coutinho asks the question, "How big is your God?" His Hindu friends and Buddhist teachers have guided him to a more mystical and more extensive view of God. I felt this way when accepting this position. Not like God, yet understanding the question: How big is your life? How big is your community? How big is your influence? How big is your God?

LEADING WITH LOVE

Now that I was working in a leadership role, I wanted to be even more intentional. I didn't want it to just happen, I wanted to decide what would happen. I had a genuine goal. I wanted to lead with conscious actions. I wanted to lead with oneness. I wanted to lead with love.

Leading with love begins with knowing ourselves and courageously being genuine about who we are. Could it be that leaders have the easiest life in the world? Is it because we work within social constructs that protect us from being real? These constructs define our patterns and shield us. We may have an easy life.

The accomplishments of leaders are often the result of behaviors that distance us from others. We rush to meet deadlines even when we know more listening is needed. We meet challenges using title, power, authority, and money rather than relationship, patience, and mutual respect. We sever ourselves from others with our fear, aggression, disingenuousness, concealment of our hurts, hiding our weaknesses, holding others at arm's length, and failing to recognize and celebrate people.

In doing this, we are isolating ourselves in our leadership and missing out on interrelatedness and our need for each other. Can a tree stand tall without the earth beneath it, the sky above it, and the light and the rain all around it? We, as human beings, need each other.

From the times of antiquity, love has been a concern of philosophers. Plato said that love is an expansion of the heart toward another human being. Should that definition be confined to a romantic relationship, or can it be expanded to fit into a business, a university, or a leadership role? One of the most famous lines from the prayer of St Francis of Assisi is: "Lord, make me an instrument of thy peace. Where there is hatred, let me sow love." Returning to person-to-person, human-to-human interaction is a profound way of sowing love. It is an expansion of the heart. Person-to-person is the epitome of "I affect you. You affect me."

We've all heard of the butterfly effect. If the beating of the wings of a tiny creature like a butterfly might affect the weather in another part of the world, imagine what your negative or positive thoughts, feelings or actions might do. The butterfly is also a powerful example of transformation. It progresses from a cocoon to a flying beauty. We couldn't see the butterfly before it emerged, yet it was there; the same as love grows when we transform and welcome it into our lives. Love grows within our organizations when we move beyond judgment and begin to perceive and see the people around us as human beings in transformation. Would we ever call an acorn stupid? Would we think it was useless and compare it to a tree? No, it has its purpose; one day, it will be the mighty oak.

Love is part of every culture; we need to look through others' eyes to learn about what they offer. We must lead with compassion. We need to walk in the shoes of others. We must set down our baggage and be like the butterfly and soar. Leading with love is about actions. It transcends boundaries; it is interconnectedness, it is being One.

Our world is hurting; love can transcend this brokenness. Love needs to be part of everything we engage in. It is beyond ourselves. Love is Oneness.

HOME

Being a single parent, a nursing student, and working was never my plan. It's a tough road to go and yet it was the road I was on. I was committed to my son, and I was committed to my future career. I could make this happen.

There's a bit of parenting advice that is highly recommended: get your child an alarm clock. The reason for this is self-reliance. If you wake them up every morning for the first eighteen years of their life, chances are they will rely on that. This one simple act, hearing and turning off the alarm and then getting up, can be the beginning of a host of other accomplishments. In the military, they say "make your bed." These simple habits can make a huge difference in one's life.

My son's life didn't start the way I had hoped. He constantly questioned me about his dad. I always tried to be positive and give Jeremy a good feeling about his father. I'm sure the hurt was buried deep inside him. From his early school years, I used to hear him crying in the shower. Maybe he needed to feel that pain in private. When hearing this crying, I felt like a failure as a mother. I'm now amazed at the remarkable man that he has become.

I don't think I even bought him an alarm clock. From about kindergarten, he would wake himself up, get himself dressed and get ready for school. He seemed to be naturally organized.

And he was highly analytical. When he was old enough to turn on the TV, he watched weather reports on three or more channels. He would then use this data to create his own weather report. He still does this today.

I tried to be the best mom. I wanted to be perfect. I wanted my son to be perfect. I knew that everyone was watching. And he too would discover this soon enough.

People are judgmental. I was judged as a single parent. I was judged as a parent who continued to pursue higher education. I was judged as a mom when everyone knew that a son needs a father figure.

This was painful—trying to stay in my lane, find my path, work my way, and yet hearing those whispers on the sidelines. I'm sure they often meant the best; it was hard to know whom to listen to. My son was the center of my whole world. Together we faced the realities that had come to us. How do we manage? How does anyone fit together the complexities of home and work?

Growing up in the time and place of my youth had lots of norms. Lots of expectations. Lots of that old favorite saying, "this is the way we've always done it." Oh, how glad I am, to have gone beyond that "hold back" saying.

I can look back at what I didn't do as a mom. I think everyone probably can. I wasn't perfect despite my intent. I can hear myself reminding Jeremy to pick up his toys before a bedtime story. I can remember the sports, the homework, the usual things. I remember taking him with me to graduate school classes or the university computer lab. These things are what make him who he is today. We were a team, and as we all know, there is no letter I in the word team. I was so lucky to have my parents, Jeremy's grandparents. We needed them so much. I appreciate them immensely. I hope that I conveyed that during those precious and challenging times.

Surrendering to my needs was one of the most important things I did. By showing my weakness and vulnerability, I was blessed with the beautiful gifts that my parents had to offer.

As a parent of a young achiever, I had some learning to do. I found that I had to learn to watch how he did things in ways I had never experienced. I had little to teach him about social activities since I was an introvert and not very social.

My little man has grown up. He is a man of his own making. He is successful on a fascinatingly different path. I love the talks we have. In conversation, he will talk about a learned experience from someone older. It's as if he's had a special gift of dancing with the elderly since he was two years old. I don't think he seeks it out. They appear in his life, and he dances with them.

Jeremy has four daughters. And now he is the parent, the teacher, the one who tries to find that balance. He tries to protect them, like I tried to protect him. It isn't the same, it's derived from love, and that is the ingredient needed.

As my son's life has unfolded, he has become the patriarch. His father has had other marriages and other sons, so Jeremy has stepbrothers and has cultivated relationships with them all. It's not traditional. It's not what I had envisioned. The father usually initiates this sort of familial connection. I'm grateful that my son honors the family and has become the glue. He has become a father to his children and also to the younger stepbrothers.

Tradition told us that family consisted of mom and dad and kids. We were supposed to tell each other that we loved them and take care of each other accordingly.

In the musical Fiddler on the Roof, the main character Tevye has his life turned upside down. Nothing happens as it was supposed to. His five daughters don't marry who he expects them to marry. And then, in his exasperation with his life he asks his wife Golde, "Do you love me?" "Do I love you?" she asks, and then goes on to sing about what she has done to show her love.

Love isn't dogmatic. Rigidity and doctrine do not define love. My son has learned to live outside the lines. He has poured forth his love in ways that Golde sings about. I am so proud.

Family doesn't end with biological ties. My extended family of friends and colleagues around the world are part of this bigger love that we are exploring.

Love is not only for family. Love is part of all of our relationships. Love needs to be part of our work. Love needs to be the centering point in leadership. And it is a loving leadership that can change the world.

ALL THINGS CHANGE

Courage, according to the dictionary, is the ability to do something that frightens us.

Spiritual courage is accepting that you are unlikely to find the answers yet keep asking them anyway.

The root of the word "courage", writes Brené Brown, is "cor", the Latin word for heart. In its earliest forms, the word courage had a different definition from today. Courage originally meant "to speak one's mind by telling all one's heart." Brené goes on to say that today we often think of courage as synonymous with being heroic. We've lost touch with the idea that speaking honestly and openly about who we are, what we're feeling, and our experiences, is the definition of courage. Heroics is often about putting our life on the line. I believe that ordinary courage puts vulnerability on the line.

During the COVID pandemic, we often heard the word "hero." We in the nursing field were called heroes. The media called us heroes because they assumed we were putting our lives on the line; it was more than the health risks on the line. The uncertainty of our days, the insecurity of our jobs, the safety of our families, and our vulnerability, were constantly put on the line.

The pandemic brought pain to everyone, and the reaches of

this ache were global. Along with educators, school staff, and mental health workers, nurses ranked high on the list of suffering. Personal traumas, injustices, threats, and disease were part of our daily battles. If this was a war, our courage got us through it.

Lockdowns had eased, vaccinations were being delivered, and hope was on the way. More and more of us were returning to work, and life was starting to change again. It was an ordinary morning in the dean's office of the University of Minnesota School of Nursing. And yet there was a funny feeling that seemed contagious. The second pot of coffee was being brewed, and this hadn't happened in two years. People were coming back. One can only know this feeling if they have experienced it themselves, and everyone has had some experience with the pandemic.

We had taken too much of life for granted. We hadn't valued seeing one another, the comradery we shared, the gatherings, meetings, graduation ceremonies, and celebrations, or even the coffee. A fundamental law of human beings is interdependence.

As a young nursing student, I used to do community home health. I drove one chilly autumn morning out to La Crosse, where an elderly woman, Mary, lived alone. She grew onions. I remember the smell upon entering her tiny little home. It was so isolated, and she was so small, and yet there she was standing at the stove, making onion soup. "Sit down deary," she'd say. "Let me get you some soup." This is one of the places I learned interdependence. I was sent out to check on her health and she handed me a bowl of onion soup. I didn't even know that I needed her, even so, I did. And I still think of Mary today. I didn't think of it as interdependence at the time and yet that is what it was.

It was during COVID that we were exposed to the long-overlooked disparities in our healthcare system. It elevated the need to focus more on wellbeing—for the patients, of course, and also for the healthcare professionals. It begged our leadership team to ask each other and face our mortality: Who might not be present the next day? COVID exposed the most severe nursing shortage in decades. It was also during this time of isolation that racial tensions blew up when the murder of George Floyd, occurring a few blocks from where I lived, highlighted the inequities and racism within our communities, our police department, our healthcare system, and the university. Business and worker shortages caused minor inconveniences for the public and critical emergencies throughout the system.

Along with COVID came extreme heat waves, cold spells, droughts and floods, wildfires, and once-in-a-lifetime storms. We lost much trust. Technology is a tool we value; truth and honesty are limited. We were inundated with misinformation and uncertainties. Do we pay attention to the health of the people or the health of the planet, or do we co-mingle, respect that interdependence and call it one?

The consequences of these dark holes in our world could be the growth of fear and suspicion, uncertainty, insecurity, and an ego-based system. We at the nursing school wanted to go differently. Not in a "we versus them" approach, rather, an "I am" and "we are" system of wholeness—a holistic approach to the future.

An American Nurses Association SmartBrief summarized: Nurses don't want to hear about self-care, resilience, and short-term stress interventions. They don't want to be fed. They want to do the fishing. They want long-term systemic change.

During World War II, nurses played a primary role in the care of soldiers. Nurses worked in military hospitals. This aided in expanding the role of nurses beyond the traditional character. Nurses returned from war as experienced medical professionals who took on new and more advanced medical procedures. Was the pandemic the new war? Why do we tend to appreciate only when the need is great? We had taken advantage of the nursing profession and COVID brought it back into the spotlight.

The COVID experience also had a profound impact on our students. They experienced the challenge of studies and campus life differently. This generation of graduates has changed the perception from all previous generations of students and teachers. Who they have become will continue to change how individuals engage and expand within their professions. They have learned to be flexible. They have learned to work alone. They have learned to live with uncertainty. And they have learned to value the whole. Learning to be a part of something bigger than oneself will change the shape of the future. We in nursing want to be at the forefront of this new way of thinking, and of being. We want a new normal. A better life, work, and world.

A Pew Research Report spells out some of our needs:

- Social justice will get priority.
- People's wellbeing will prevail over profit.
- The quality of life for disabilities will improve and inspire other enhancements.
- Artificial intelligence, virtual reality, augmented reality, deep learning, and machine learning will yield well.
- Smarter systems will be created.

This list can make a better world. As leaders in healthcare and education, we will be proactive, not simply responders. These challenges won't be sitting on a "to-do"' list, they will be the blaze that occupies our souls and propels change. We will help create a vibrant future.

Admiral Grace Hopper said, "The most damaging phrase in the English language is, 'we've always done it this way'". She stressed the need to constantly think forward rather than look backward. Grace Hopper was a pioneering computer scientist working in a fast-moving technological field. She knew that resistance to change was detrimental. This is especially applicable in times of disruption. COVID brought this to a head.

One of our alumni and a school donor recently questioned me on our shared experiences during the pandemic. She reminded me that when we lose someone or something, we experience grief. And it was grief that indeed we were feeling. We had gone through denial, anger, bargaining, depression, and acceptance. Accepting and processing our grief allowed us to develop plans for the future. We have learned to honor others' time. What we took for granted is now appreciated. We value our community. It was losing it that inspired us to prop it up and build on it, nurture it, and revitalize it. By nurturing our wellbeing, we are creating healthier ways of being at one with each other, working together, and impacting the world as leaders. As a force fueled by synergy—not by the old model of me, me, me—WE will be the difference. WE keep asking the questions. WE have the courage.

FLOW

"The greatest thing in this world is not so much where we stand, as in what direction we are moving: To reach the port of heaven, we must sometimes sail with the wind and sometimes against it—but we must sail, and not drift, nor lie at anchor."

Oliver Wendell Holmes

A recent McKinsey report says that "history shows that in times of disruption, resilience depends on adaptability and decisiveness." Oliver Wendell Holmes was a champion of this thinking. Born in 1809, Holmes was a successful physician, anatomy and physiology professor at Harvard, dean of the Harvard medical school, and accomplished poet. It is his poetry that still sways us today.

We at the University of Minnesota felt strong winds. Winds we hadn't planned for, and that took us by surprise. And yet I can't help thinking about all the opportunities that the COVID wind gave us. We were forced to adapt and think in new ways. We did this with a decisiveness that put us on a tack in a new direction. We could not only stand by our old reputation; we needed to move, pull up the anchor, and sail.

When I think of this forward movement, I am reminded of flow. Being in a flow state is described as the mental state in which a person performing some activity is fully immersed in energized focus. It is absorption in what one does. And I have learned this from the greats like Oliver Wendell Holmes and also from my sister Ann.

Ann was born with Down's syndrome. She carries an excitement and zest for life that I wish everyone shared. We got together recently and viewed some of our favorite old movies. We watched We Bought a Zoo, and Ann was fully immersed. She was focused. In the film, the father has been grieving the loss of his wife, and his son has been expelled from school. The family's situation was not working, things were getting dire. The whole family was wallowing in their grief, nonetheless, it was going from that painful grieving process and getting through it that makes the film great. The family makes the most unlikely decision to purchase a zoo. They repair their crumbling relationships by building a better model within their home and their community. This life story of moving forward, being resilient, and being decisive captures the viewer and takes us from tragedy to exhilaration. And Ann gets it. She doesn't need to take a class on focus or wellbeing, she doesn't worry about her image, and she never holds back on her beaming smile, honest love, and being in the present. She holds the story in her hand and pays it forward. She is flow.

I was gifted with another example of this open "pay it forward" nature from a surprise visit to our university. A gentleman in blue jeans, scruffy long hair, and a lackadaisical demeanor walked into the School of Nursing office. As an assistant looked up from her desk about to ask his business, he spoke before her and said he wanted to make a gift to the nursing school. Nursing had always been critical to him.

By the looks of him and the unscheduled visit, we were skeptical. This kind of first impression judgment is sad, and I hate even to think that I do this. I believe it happens unintentionally and comes from bad habits. I have worked to rid myself of this kind of judgment, and we also work within our school to develop a non-biased approach towards oneness.

We welcomed him in, and as our development team got to know the man, they learned that he was a Vietnam veteran, had some health issues, and was sorting out his life. Everything must go, he said. This man was not drifting and certainly wasn't lying at anchor. He wanted to give his home to Habitat for Humanity with the condition that it be gifted to a vet. He lived a very simple life and was planning a simple departure.

We were all surprised by the huge gift he bestowed upon the nursing school scholarship program. I was honored to get to know him through my periodic meetings. He was shy, humble, and generous. One day I mentioned that I would love it if he would accept my invitation to come to the meeting we hold twice a semester with all the staff and faculty of our school. I asked if he would come and sit in the room with me. He could observe and didn't have to give a talk. I wanted to share my thoughts and feelings with the faculty and staff. And he came. We all sat at the front of a large conference room with more than a hundred staff and faculty attending. Our new friend, genuine as always, wore his blue jeans and long hair with quiet confidence. I introduced him and thanked him for supporting our students. He made a few comments about nursing and the caring he had experienced. We all thanked him, and he left. After walking him out and thanking him once again, especially for the courage to join such a group, I returned to a room buzzing with the wave this man had created.

This could have been an awkward setting for him. Taking a seat in front of a crowd of academic hierarchy at an institution where rank is established by degrees and titles, he did not look like he fitted in. We all learned that it is the new winds that blow through our trees that help plant the future. His humble life, simple story, and peaceful presence were still there in that room. People were talking. They were in awe. And instead of moving through the meeting agenda, a spontaneity came through me.

"You know, isn't it curious," I said, "that we are a School of Nursing, and we never use the word love." This was not a planned item on my agenda; it was a flame that had been lit, and it caught on fire. This unexpected visitor reminded us of the power of love, the uniqueness of every individual, and the duty we have to be open enough to accept it. The staff and faculty were animated. They understood. Nurses work with people. They listen, they care, they love, and they are present. Nurses experience deep intimacy with patients and families. This kind of connection and caring doesn't always need words. It's just there. Its presence is understood.

I believe that love is the underlying force that flows through this magnificent world. And it is the love generated by our faculty and staff that makes our students, graduates, and institution shine. It flows.

A friend of mine told me a story of her time in the hospital as a child. "I had terrible asthma," she said, "and it landed me in the hospital on several occasions. And what I remember most about those visits was the back rubs. I don't think they do it anymore. As the dinner trays were taken away and the last medications were given out, the lights dimmed, and the nurses made their final rounds before we were bid to sleep. I lay in my bed with sweet young hope. I knew I would be getting better, and I would have a wonderful sleep once I got my back rub. The nurse would come in and take up the little plastic bottle that sat on the bedside table. 'Turn on to your stomach,' she'd say, and I did it with complete trust. She squeezed the cream into those caring hands of hers and started to massage it into my back. The strain was lifted, the worry was dissipated, and a perfect calm took over my body. Sleep beckoned.

"A final healing touch from the nurse, and she quietly left. I was only a young girl at the time, yet this has stayed with me. I have held on to that feeling and remember this gift like it was yesterday. This wasn't about duty. This was an example of a love emanating from a professional who knew there was more to her job than what was written in the textbooks. For this, I am grateful."

My friend's memory epitomizes the need for leaders to think and feel with head and heart. Using both head and heart helps create relationships, and it is relationship that is the most significant and essential component of nursing. I can list the attributes of presence, support, honesty, intimacy, healing, collaboration, responsiveness, and even sacrifice. The actuality of my friend's story proves what nursing is about.

It is these same qualities that we need in all of our organizations. They are necessary for healthy leadership. They are essential for a better world.

Our nursing school is a living laboratory. I now use the word love in everyday conversation. It is part of the motivation that feeds our actions. As a dean of the School of Nursing, I know that stagnation inhibits, and I do not hesitate to use the word love in meetings, classrooms, walking down hallways, chatting with students and staff, faculty, and executives. I can say that I loved a freshly picked cherry cobbler as well as I can say that I loved our discussion. I felt love from someone dropping me a note.

We all regularly comment on how we think about the love of a family. And we are proud when we see one of ours who demonstrates love to the patients. Love is omnificent, and that is the direction we are headed.

HOW DO WE DO THIS?

How do we change the character—one might say culture—of an organization? How do we change the organizational drive from "me" and "money" to "we" and "honey"? I use the image of honey because it represents pleasure, sweetness, truth, and knowledge. And also because it flows. Honey has often been associated with prosperity and abundance. Moses led his people out of Egypt into the land of milk and honey. Can we lead our people into a land of oneness? A land that flows like honey? A place where "we" is the norm? To do this, we have to be able to flow, to bend.

We all grew up with traditions. Some of these traditions are beneficial, and others tend to hurt people. Our businesses, organizations, universities, and even households, have lived through hierarchies for many years. One person at the top tells the others what to do. They follow orders or else. They increase the business's profit, the organization's value, and they take the university up to the highest levels of grandeur. The purpose is to win, and this often creates a loser.

When I was growing up, I played trumpet in a band. Creating music is a win-win situation. Everyone plays their own instrument. They make their own sound and their own string of notes. They make up the flow. In the end, it's the transformation of twenty, or fifty, or a hundred different players that when conducted with precision turns into a single and beautiful creation.

When I arrived at the University of Minnesota in 2005, I was asked to lead an extensive nursing school transformation. The faculty and staff had high aspirations, and they wanted it to happen fast. I had committed to making this happen, and it was my history—my being part of a team on a family farm with aspirations to impact the world, my playing in a band, and my not always fitting in—that lent itself to the transformation toward this mission. I would be conducting an orchestra and the music would be filled with love.

Dichotomies, polarities, and dualities exist for a reason. How can they be used or integrated for transformation? Oppositions create success. We cannot have light without dark, and we cannot create a whole without connecting the many parts. When I started working with the team on the changes requested and needed at the school, I was committed to welcoming and thrashing out the negative factors. We did not ignore them; we used these differences to create something more significant. How can we ask our foot to walk if we don't bend the knee? We have to look at and appreciate different perspectives. We learn from resistance. We grow from challenges, and we transform with interdependence. For me, it was opening myself and letting people in that invited others to do the same. By being vulnerable, we set the bar where it isn't so low that it's easy to get over, yet not so high that we run into it and fall. Remember, Brené Brown's definition of vulnerability is not winning or losing; it is the courage to show up and be seen when we have no control over the outcome. It's not weakness; it's a measure of courage. I knew that our faculty, staff, and nurses had the courage, and I was confident that transformation was not only a desire, it was a need.

Nursing is critical to the healthcare industry. It is essential to the health of individuals and communities. Not only do nurses provide patient care, they also support health education. They are constantly teaching and sharing their knowledge with patients and their families. They teach disease prevention and treatments, and offer guidance and help with long term conditions. They help patients make informed decisions.

Many nurses go beyond the carer/patient role by working in research. In hospitals, clinics, schools, community health centers and universities, nurses take on leadership roles. They serve as administrators and educators. They create policy and they work towards a better healthcare system in the future. Nurses show vulnerability every day because they show up every day. The school needed a transformation and in looking at the love that nurses have shown naturally, I knew we could spread this love to create a wider and more effective school. We had the tools; we needed to use them to their best advantage.

Transformation was the essence. Creating a greater whole being fed with love was the goal, for our university and for the planet. If we are educating future caregivers and healers, our "job" is our essence—our serious core.

We need to lead with love.

GIVE UP OR BEND

After the loss of my husband, I too was lost. I drove away from my parent's farm one day going nowhere. My mind was frazzled, and my days were a blur. I was a lonely single mom and felt hopeless among the people in our small community. It felt like they were all looking at me and saying, "she's the one. She's that girl whose husband ran away." This was too hard to bear. As I drove along the familiar yet lonesome road and gazed at the mighty oaks, I realized I am not an oak. I am not strong. I no longer have the values that were my anchor. I can't do it. I shouldn't be here. I have no life. I'm nothing. End it. Just end it. In that very late sunset evening I drove away from those haughty, strong oak trees and stopped in a remote field. I could relate more to the empty bareness of the field than to anything tough and mighty. The station wagon with Jeremy's blanket, books, and toys, had a perfect place to lie down in the back. I could end it here. My parents could raise my child. Would this be the end of my story? What good are stories anyway? I grew up on stories, and I loved them. Aesop's fables were full of morals. Morality was not in my head at the time. I kept thinking of the strength I didn't have. However, in one of Aesop's fables, a tall, strong oak tree is on the bank of a river near some reeds. The oak tree was proud of its strength and size. One day, as the wind started blowing, the oak tree mocked the reeds as they moved to and fro with the slightest breeze. The reeds kept quiet and continued to sway back and forth. "Look at me; I am so strong and mighty," said the oak tree. The wind got furious and turned into a hurricane. The reeds continued to bow and sway with the rhythm of the wind. The oak tree tried fighting with the wind and was soon uprooted and thrown into the river.

I could be like the reeds. I had no pride left. However, humility is indeed worth something. It is better to bend than to break. Better to be flexible than stubborn. I thought that I was broken. Staring up at that magnificent sky and brilliant stars, surrounded by the nature with which I was so in tune, realizing that I could bend like the reeds and surrender to the wind, I floated out of myself at that moment. Looking down at myself, I knew what I had to do. I knew what I wanted to do. This is my story. I can end it, or I can use this moment as a starting point. I could feel a lift. A draining of the sludge bogging me down was replaced by a healthy emptiness that felt like a positive light, a kind of freedom. And it wasn't only about me. I had a beautiful energetic son. I was incredibly blessed to have this special little person in my life and I wanted to be here for him. I was on my way up. Through complete surrender, I re-engaged in this world. I could, and was, starting anew.

This is where I became acquainted with a new positivity—a positivity that grows out of deeply painful human experiences. I had been dwelling and drowning in all the negatives. I plodded away on the heavy path of negativity instead of remembering my essence, counting my blessings, and moving toward love. My parents and family loved me, my child loved me, and I would learn to love myself again. Joseph Campbell said, "Find a place inside where there's joy, and the joy will burn out the pain." My son was my joy. I moved to the front of the car and drove back home. I knew things wouldn't be easy, and yet I was at peace, and looking forward to the journey ahead.

It wasn't easy. Despite deciding to live, my life was in fragments. Those eyes—those beautiful brown eyes of my little boy looking at me and asking me when his daddy was coming home! His look, his plea, his innocence pierced me in the heart. I cried, and I tried. I tried so hard. I wanted to give him hope and told him that his dad loved him. Saying it is much easier than feeling it. I fell into a deep depression. I had no idea that mental anguish could be so painful. While I had looked upon people with physical maladies in the past, I'd never seen inside someone's aching soul. I was doing the same to myself. What I could not see and feel in myself, I could not see or feel in others.

And then there was the questioning. My brain was in overdrive as I asked myself what went wrong. Could I have been a better wife? Was I not worthy? Was it my fault? I badgered myself. I blamed myself. I threw myself to the wolves of devastation. I fed these wolves with my banter. I indulged in self-harm, not physical, just an emotionally devastating crash.

Every time a wave crashes upon a shore, there is a respite. The water slowly flows back out to sea. Calm ensues. And I kept waiting for the waves to diminish, for the peace I needed. I knew it was there.

When I opted for life, the first thing I did was drive home. And that is the key to almost everything. Home. We've all seen the little board on the shelf painted with rose-colored letters saying that home is where the heart is. Wall hangings are abundant in my part of the world, and crocheted into many of them is the same message: home is where the heart is. I had driven home; however, I couldn't find my heart. It was home, and it was the love and daily talks with my parents and siblings that lifted my heart back up to its full vibrating vigor. This didn't happen overnight. Going home and having the support of loved ones helped bring me back from the abyss where I had fallen.

I felt freedom once I realized the potential that I had. No one and no circumstance were going to hold me back. I am meant to be here. I will become the person that I was always meant to be. I couldn't help think back to that oak tree. Could it have really begun as an acorn? If that tree was always in that acorn, I could surely rise to my potential from this lowliest place where I found myself.

I had been studying nursing when this occurred. Once I could get up in the morning, hold up my head, and walk out the door with hope, I shared with the dean of my school (Sister Grace Clare) what had happened. I told her I did not know where my husband was. It was time for me to quit. She said "No. You are to be here. You need to finish your BSN with majors in nursing and mathematics. We are here to support you and be flexible through these days of unknowing." And she found a way to keep me in school, helping me with financial and academic pressures. She could have said, "Our thoughts and prayers are with you." Wouldn't that have been a different ending? The compassion, thoughtful guidance, help, and confidence in me that the school gave me paved the way out of my depression. I was given another chance.

I worked at being a good mother, I worked at being a good student, and I worked at separating myself from my husband Craig and beginning a new chapter. I worked at clearing out the past. And in that process I became aware that one's life is a tapestry. All pieces matter, all pieces create a beautiful whole. Mainly I was learning that to deny a piece or part denies the whole and denies gratitude for the learnings that come with dualities. I couldn't continue holding on to this anger, so I sent Craig a letter. I thanked him. I told him that I was made whole again through the experience of his departure. I had been a fragmented piece of his life, and now I was a vibrant individual. This unexpected explosion of relationship and commitment had blown me into a new, healthier, and more congruent trajectory and I wanted to thank him. I wished him well.

If I were to see him today, I would wish him well. Most likely our discussions would re-anchor into the shared growing-up years, our multi-generational family ties, our shared school, and college memories. This change of attitude and action did not come quickly. It was a few years before I wrote that letter. Time does heal. And finding that light in oneself, that spark that grows when given the breath it needs, the love of others, and the love of one's self—this is what makes it happen.

I must give thanks to the field of nursing. I am so grateful. Because of the hope I had, because of the future I now saw of me actually becoming a nurse, and because of the serving, giving and loving nature of this profession, the thought alone took me forward. Nursing became pivotal to my recovery. My son was in my heart and nursing was in my soul. I really felt I was on my way.

SO HOW DO I BEGIN?

What I learned in Kindergarten

In Yoga, they say, we don't compete, we improve. In a competitive domain, with a philosophy of capitalism and an "I'll prove that I'm the best" kind of world, how do we lead with love? How do we improve the "we" and not only the "me"?

Many leadership styles involve charging in and showing one's power, maybe even intimidating people to get things done. This was not my way, and I put great thought into how I would welcome this huge leadership position. Everything I had experienced in my life came into play. Being a member of a band as a student, living on a family farm as a youngster, having the experience of "nothing could be worse" after the departure of my husband, learning to flow like the reeds, being flexible like the people who allowed me the leeway to continue my studies, and the love I'd received from my family and co-workers—these were the tools I'd start with. The incredible nursing experiences in the ICU and the increased attention and import of informatics gave me the head and heart to get started.

I believe I'm a humble person; I am not weak. I am grounded. I am human. I will make mistakes, and I will do my best.

Before I arrived at the University of Minnesota, the faculty and staff of the School of Nursing wrote an in-depth report detailing their aspirations for their school and how the new dean would nurture and appropriate this plan. This solid set of expectations gave me a reference point of who they were, where people wanted to go, and what they wanted to accomplish.

As a child starting kindergarten in the morning, you walk into the classroom, wash your hands, put your name in the box, sit at your table, smile, and then listen.

When heading to my office as dean of the School of Nursing, I walked into the building, washed my hands, announced my name, sat at my desk, smiled, and then listened. Important things are really not that different. Both learning and leading involve showing up, and listening.

Have you ever read about a new coach being hired for a team? Coaches are all about success. They are hired to take their team to victory. No other abstractions. They don't need to have the best hairstyle or uniforms or humor. They are meant to win. And as I thought about coaching, I thought about the direction I wanted to take this nursing school which I had the great honor of guiding. What kind of game were we playing? Were there rules? Was there a beginning and an end? Or was this an infinite game? A game that kept on playing; where the importance was staying in the game rather than winning. Simon Sinek talks about this in his book, The Infinite Game. He says that when we lead with a finite mindset in an infinite game, it leads to all kinds of problems, the most common of which include the decline of trust, cooperation, and innovation. Groups that adopt an infinite mindset enjoy higher levels of trust, cooperation, and innovation. We are not out to win. We are here to continue—to build a nursing school into a world-class facility for learning opportunities, innovation, exploration, and the ultimate task of delivering the best possible health care. We are in for the long game.

So how was I to adapt this infinite mindset? How was I going to take nursing to the next dimension? Nursing is not about a set of rules that end with a win. Of course, we want a patient to get better. We want to use our expertise to administer the very best in medications, treatments, and follow-ups for a successful recovery, although that is not the end. We eventually even learned that environment plays a role in recovery. And because of these new discoveries, it excites us to keep learning. A person, a patient, a human being, does not end after recovery. Life goes on. And if we can help with the growth of said human life, then that is an infinite game. That is a new mindset. That is transformation and the turning the "I am a nurse" into "We are the future." It is not about me, it's about We. That is our goal.

Do we do it alone, or do we ask for help?

So yes, we engaged outside help. Yes, we agreed to and encouraged studies to look at our potential.

We had goals. We wanted to grow. We aspired to be in the top ten nursing schools in the country. We asked for help. And I believe that asking for help is one of the greatest prescriptions for success. I had committed to a bold transformation. I didn't come with a set agenda. I did look at and listen to what it was that the school wanted to achieve. I couldn't do it alone so we called on an outside organization and it was their help with an analysis that set us on our way.

I honored and respected the school's team who had generated plans for the future. I looked at their proposals, I took in the information from the outside source and I said that I was ready to make it happen. I was ready to be part of a big new plan, an exciting growth for the school.

Sometimes one is surprised by the "ordinary". I was originally skeptical about the hiring of an outside agency. The Management Analysis and Development (MAD) team we had hired for advice was fabulous. My perceptions were wrong. Their hard work and analysis were spectacular.

The analysis team proposed redesigning organizational structures and reporting. They suggested changes in information technology, human resources, resource management, budget accountability, and internal and external communications. The list was detailed and extensive.

By sharing these suggestions with members of the faculty and staff, we created immediate transparency. I was not going to sit in an office ticking off things I'd accomplished. These challenges were to be worked on as a team, and I was able to leverage the power, insights, and wisdom of the faculty and staff as they came up with ideas. We have a job to do, and we will accomplish it together. Leading is not about being on top; I believe it's about getting everyone to know and feel that they can and do make a difference—that they have contributed. I had the confidence and the humility to proceed, and so did our team.

After eighteen months of tackling the suggestions made by MAD, we had the MAD team return and reassess our progress. We had achieved the recommended goals. We had addressed every one of the priorities. We did it! Change is possible and rapid change is achievable. We had defied expectations and assumptions that seem to exist across much of higher education and many organizations—that life in a bureaucracy moves slowly. Not in the School of Nursing. We move fast.

Early in our reorganization efforts, we engaged another outside organization, Creative Health Care Management (CHCM). In partnership with us, we invited them to adapt and conduct a nursing practice program on leading an empowered organization (LEO). Every faculty and staff member in the school was invited to participate, and almost everyone engaged. The time we spent together changed our organization. It was the true beginning of empowering everyone. We recognized that all the faculty and staff in the School of Nursing are leaders. Title or position matter little compared to who we are together and acknowledging the community as a whole, as a "We are." It was the decentralization of power that created a new voice. Everyone's voice works together—one voice.

This approach wasn't asking an outside organization to make the changes. It was in partnership with CHCM that we achieved harmony and transformation. Asking for help is humbling, and humility is a stepping stone to success.

Since this initial use of consultants, we have rarely needed to engage additional ones. We prioritize transformation and innovation with everyone on our team. Working with both faculty and staff became a core principle in the changes we made in the school. Faculty are no more critical than staff, and staff is no more important than faculty. Team members trust one another. They work together towards a common goal. They hold themselves accountable, and the other members as well. I had learned positivity the hard way. It was a sure catalyst for the success of our work. When a team has a positive dynamic, the members are more creative, supportive, and successful.

As I emphasized when I began, the absolute authority of leaders is not dominant power. Our most significant influence is bringing people together, maintaining focus, and supporting the goals of the organization and beyond. Our passion is constantly guiding people to discern and honor the more significant impact of their own power and creativity. We repeatedly rehearse to accomplish our common purpose.

I like to bring people together and foster connections. I tap them on the shoulder, nudging them, and give them little lifts, all done invisibly. I still enjoy moving in the background. When I do need to be visible, it is not hierarchical. I anchor myself in the realities of the situation. I am the leader. We are the solution. I am the dean. We are the school. And as the "We" gets bigger and stronger, I dissolve.

Most of my actual clinical practice was as an intensive care nurse. This calling permeated my soul, and it still does. I also had to unlearn the habits of rapid response and respect the evolution of change. Emergency response works and is necessary for the intensive care unit and certain events in life; however, it is less called for in the community life of an organization. It is less called for in society in general. To create a successful organization like the School of Nursing, the drama and the rapid response I was

used to was not necessary.
Teamwork does not mean letting things just happen. I do intentionally engage in micromanagement. This is deliberate and often occurs when maintaining stability and focusing on an unwavering direction. I stay directly involved in new initiatives until the rhythm is set. I remain close when someone begins a new leadership position which reports to me. I immediately engage when an issue is raised. I am there when there is a concern about the direction or complexity of issues. I believe in a hands-on approach. This is different from a "do what I say" tactic.
We know how it feels when someone is aggressive, wanting to seize power and control. These actions create ripples in the flow of an organization. They create hurdles people need to jump and shouldn't have to. Many times, this aggressiveness comes from a lack of respect. In our initiative to make every position meaningful, to not have a top-down, trickle-down kind of system, I prioritize being aware of this kind of aggression and intervening before it becomes toxic.
As a leader, it is important to me that I assess and am aware of my ego and constantly have a sense of the "I am", radiating from my essence, and I think it's essential for each team member as well.
Ego doesn't have a place in our organization. Our goal is more important than one individual's ego.
If we are open to the essence of who we are, of who I am, then we can use that essence to make a difference in this world. We can only give what we have, and recognizing that is so important.
I can't help relating to the Peace Pilgrim. Mildred Lisette Norman grew up on a farm with her close extended family. She later suffered through an unhappy marriage. After being the first woman to hike the entire Appalachian trail, she had a vision. This guided her for the rest of her life. She gave up her name and possessions, and wearing simple clothing in her new identity, the Peace Pilgrim

walked across America for the next twenty-eight years. She walked for peace. She met with people throughout the country with joy and purpose.

The Peace Pilgrim was the epitome of knowingness. She knew who she was and what she had to do. She acted on her purpose. We too, with intellectual humility and a more positive purpose, can have a productive influence on this world. Who am I, and what is my purpose?

A friend of mine is learning to free dive. The diver must learn to hold their breath for a very long time. The key to holding one's breath is not bravado. It's not even practicing it over and over. The key is relaxation. By slowing down the body, relaxing the whole system, and then taking in a deep breath, one can hold it much longer. I use this when dealing with unrest, aggression, or crisis. I have learned to remain relaxed. I maintain my head-heart connection. I remain centered and focused. Even in the most painful, adversarial situations, I stay in that core space of essence. Sometimes this happens instantaneously; it often takes days to resolve the problem. It takes hard work. It takes communication with the executive team and anyone at all involved. If we're sailing into port and the storm has got us rocking, our command of the calm will help us focus on the beacon and return to the flow.

There are all kinds of information written today about loneliness. People need other people. It's essential for both our physical and mental health. And if a community is vital to individuals, it certainly holds true that it is necessary for organizations.

We want our school to be a community. And creating a community requires letting go of power in the traditional sense. Whenever we grab more power through our actions or our words, we trigger others' survival instincts. It becomes a fightback situation.

Oneness requires laying down our individual agendas and efforts to dominate. It's replacing our single-minded ego with a "We."

It's creating good habits. It is not jumping to quick conclusions or a couple of brilliant thoughts that create an abundant atmosphere. It is the habits we learn and put into action. Drop by drop, step by step, positive action followed by positive action; these are the habits we develop and use in our development. Developing connections, giving away power, and acknowledging others; these all make for a stronger chain: a more powerful potential and a more loving community.

SHARING THE LIGHT

In the School of Nursing, we don't hire stars, in the usual sense. We hire people who excel in their area of expertise and possess an additional exceptional quality. We want them to shine as a We, not alone. We want them to be part of our solar system of light—a continuation and growth of what we have.

As in every organization, we work through a diligent hiring process. By diving deep and exploring each individual's nuances, we can discover the real person. We want to know their core, their purpose, and their essence.

With faculty candidates, I only have thirty minutes for an interview. I come to that meeting believing that no encounter is an accident. We are each here for a purpose that we might or might not be able to articulate. As the leader of our school, I trust you at the moment. I have that brief time to find out what we share. How we might add to this person's life and how they might add to ours. How they will fit into this growing, evolving community.

In higher education, typical interview questions revolve around research, funding, and teaching: Tell me what you've done. What are your unique contributions? Tell me about your ability to secure funding. I've already assessed these facts on paper by the time I meet with the candidate. So instead, I focus my interactive time on honoring every person as a human being and discovering their core.

I regularly start by addressing the candidate's questions and letting them know they and their questions are of key importance.

I follow up by asking three questions. They are not directly related to the usual metrics of higher education. They are about life. They are about this individual with whom I am engaging:

1. When you are one hundred and fifty years old, what do you most want to be known for? This question has an edge. Do you know your purpose? How willing and able are you to share that principle?
2. What do you do for fun? This question addresses a key part of how we live together. Whether we're together in person or virtually, we're more than professors, researchers, and administrators. The School of Nursing engages a significant portion of our lives. Are you more than your work? What is your work-life integration?
3. If you join our faculty—and I am your dean—how would I know if you're unhappy? I listen for the person who can say "I will tell you." That signals to me that they have the courage to speak up. They are transparent.

Some candidates say that I will be able to tell if I watch their expressions. From that, you will know that I'm not doing well. And here's how I discern that response. As a dean, I'm holding several thousand people in my awareness. I can be available and sensitive; however, I don't read minds. I quickly get a sense of how easily a person can communicate their feelings that matter to the function of our school. As a school family, we highlight the safety of expression, voice, and assertiveness. Regarding an individual's happiness in a large organization, the one who speaks out will get the attention the quickest.

Talking about money follows all other discussions. While

important, it follows purpose, essence, and commitment to the community. Is the candidate challenged to honor long-time, highly productive faculty and staff? Is the individual moved to respond to special requests for salary? I'm not a person who bargains and negotiates on offers. Being a salesperson is not my genius. I don't go back and forth on salary negotiations. I know that many professionals are taught to drive a hard deal. While I recognize that as standard practice, I don't believe it's helpful to the candidate or the community. I know that this can be risky.

When I say that I don't negotiate, I also convey that the offer I make is the best I can do. This is one way I communicate value and respect for the candidate. My best offer is a concrete way of showing honor.

In higher education, as in other sectors, it is common for someone to seek monetary commitments that exceed guidelines. They believe they are such a magnificent star that they should be compensated significantly higher than others. However, I've had entry-level candidates request the salary of full professors with long, very productive careers. The amount they ask is far beyond the benchmarks. We are happy that we can financially provide for wonderful tenured people who have contributed to the school for decades. I hear that you are valuable, I will say to the candidate. You will bring wonderful gifts with you. However, I have to decline your salary request. I would disrespect all these other magnificent people if I said yes to you. They are magnificent like you, and they have been advancing the mission for decades.

Whether it's the old-timers or the newcomers, we celebrate each other. Those who lack the commitment to a purpose beyond self and community don't fit in. As leaders, we need to hold all the qualities we expect from our candidates. We expect as much or more from ourselves as we expect from them. High on the list of must-haves is our ability to function in a team as leaders and essential contributors. We constantly ask ourselves these questions:

- How do I live out a belief in the richness of each human contributor on our team?
- What is my attitude toward my stardom and uniqueness?
- How can I contribute to the community rather than be ego-focused?
- What do I want to be remembered for?
- How do I live out an integrated work-life balance?
- How do I let my team into the realities of my life?

You can be a star. However, if the community element isn't genuinely important to you, then it's a non-negotiable way in which you lead. This isn't a fit for a healthy organization. You're out of the flow. Love is missing. By centering on the whole, I can lead with love. I unwaveringly anchor myself in the richness and beauty of each of us as a unique human being, thereby bringing this uniqueness together to make something more significant.

One might wonder why I even talk about who and how we hire. For years, organizations, churches, countries, families—the list goes on—operate from a top-down system. The person at the top makes the decisions, and the organization flounders or flies accordingly. An aggressive top-down leadership style can create success despite a toxic atmosphere. How long does this last and what kind of effect does it have on the employees? If leading as part of a team, rather than a dictator, harmony follows, and toxicity has no place. I don't negotiate when hiring someone because I'm not padding my ego and not hiring to change the color of our mission. I'm engaging in order to enhance the color. To brighten the direction we're already going. So no, I don't hire free-flying stars. We do hire the best and the brightest lights we can find, and they help us all shine.

MONEY OR MINDFULNESS?

Anyone serving as a dean of a large organization constantly looks at what drives success. In our school, we have determined how we work with each other and move toward our common goal, and this determines our successes. This movement, unlike in many organizations, is not primarily defined by money.

Money doesn't buy happiness. We've all heard this saying, is it true? Studies show that happiness does rise with income, and it peaks. There is a Princeton study that showed happiness peaks at about $75,000. A later study put it up at $160,000, and still others predict great happiness for millionaires. The fact is that these studies show a very tiny effect on happiness. The key does not lie with money. Gratitude and social connections have a much bigger impact on happiness, and creating connections and real relationships is what our work is about. When I ask for money, it is with mindfulness, purpose, and a plan that has a bigger impact than for me alone. An individual who wants to be part of this kind of work environment will be happy. The money is a tool, not the end, and certainly not the factor that makes a good employee, or a happy person. A mindful individual will make a difference to the whole.

I have been told that my approach to securing funding for the nursing school is naïve. I share with the university board of regents—the university's highest decision-making body—that the School of Nursing lives in a culture of abundance. When the cause and purpose are right, money follows.

That's not how it usually unfolds in higher education. The usual approach is appealing for funds, emphasizing what can't be accomplished due to a lack of funds, and prioritizing scarcity. This scenario exists within schools, colleges, universities, and other public and private organizations. It's repeated over and over in most state legislatures and national and international organizations.

When a team is excelling, sponsors come. When shoes are durable and comfortable, the buyer arrives. When a car is efficient and reliable, the sales go up. When a house is gorgeous and in the perfect neighborhood, a bidding war ensues. And when we lead our School of Nursing true to our purpose, the money doesn't lead; it follows.

I live and foster a different starting point. I share that I'm not here to ask you for money. I'm here to illustrate how the nursing school is an integral part of this university, and how we contribute not only to the university. We also contribute to the people of Minnesota and beyond.

When I ask for money, it's always connected to a specific purpose aligned with the missions of the university and the School of Nursing. I hold myself and our school accountable for showing how that investment will be honored, usually under budget and time, and returned.

We don't look at the money as an ego measure—it is a resource. The underlying goal is not the size of the budget. It is the mission and service to those we serve, and it is what we want to do with resources. Breaking it down, what initiatives are we starting? What efforts are we trying to bring to completion? How would money empower the people already on the team or those we want to engage? What impact are we creating in the world outside this organization? If we think we need a hundred million dollars in the next two quarters, why? What is the potential impact?

When I engaged in my post-doctoral studies, I had an excellent opportunity to go to the University of Utah and work with the first formally trained nurse informatician and with one of the best health systems in the United States. At the time, it was cutting-edge in terms of informatics, bringing together data with patient outcomes. Data was at the core. What appealed to me wasn't the technology alone. It was the information and knowledge that could be extracted from the data.

It's easy for people to see spreadsheets and databases—big data. In reality, isn't it all about the challenges we can solve? About possibilities? And most of all, about people? About seeing the people and their circumstances; the people of healthcare, their care, and the interrelatedness of it all. This is much bigger than a spreadsheet.

During the depths of COVID, it was tempting to contract, pull back, retreat, bury our heads in the sand, and maybe even hibernate. Given the overload and burnout everyone was experiencing, was it time to pull back? In the School of Nursing, we looked at it differently. We held our course. We didn't wait to see what was going to happen. We made things happen.

We asked:

- "How do we want things to be?" instead of saying "I wonder how things will be?"
- "What is our vision?" instead of "I'm trying to see what's out there."
- "Why are we here?" instead of "I think I'm lost."
- "What are we learning?" instead of "I'm full to the brim."

How do we feel the pain yet not be depleted? Instead of ignoring and not recognizing what's happening, some wanted to spread the message that we shouldn't hope and dream. They questioned envisioning what the future could be. With COVID and all the financial demands the university was facing, we should expect years of recovery, people said with an air of despondency. "Please don't say that," I repeated. We need to keep dreaming. We are going to keep working toward the things that matter. We might need to reprioritize. Our focus will remain on co-creating the future, even in the most challenging times.

During the depths of COVID, the School of Nursing was engaged in the largest campaign in its history. In 2000, the school had raised five million dollars in the first campaign it had engaged in—a huge success. Our recent campaign, only the second in the school's history, raised forty-eight million dollars. It was a team effort. The appeal involved all of us. We were co-creating with confidence in the school, its direction, and what people's contributions would mean to the school and university, to higher education, and to nursing. Much of the money will be for scholarships. Other dollars will be spent to advance the school's research trajectory and innovation.

The dean's discretionary funds also skyrocketed.

So, what will we create? It's possible for faculty to hear forty-five million and wonder what's in it for them. Or the thought could be: what's in it for the dean? There's so much more at stake. This goes back to purpose, the bigger picture, and our need to use resources and ethical stewardship wisely. We value abundance, and with it comes responsibility.

I negotiated many additional faculty positions when I joined the school as dean. However, my commitment was first to assess how resources were being used. My informatics background drove a unique approach as I was teaming with a colleague at Iowa to use predictive analytics, which we had previously used on non-academic initiatives. While these fantastic computational techniques are more common today, no one then had applied them in a school of nursing setting of higher education.

We paused, completed our innovative project, and examined dimensions of faculty characteristics, course load, research load, financial data, and more. We completed dozens of models and discovered that if we rearranged how and when courses are taught, we would save almost ten faculty full-time equivalents. We had the data and the modeling evidence. We continue to examine financials every year for every course, every specialty, and every degree program. We know which courses, specialties, and degree programs might not be solvent and which ones are. We can discern why. We discern challenges. We can ask ourselves if the current state is okay. We continuously look at the whole.

The depth of these analyses is highly unusual in the academic environment, although we've been doing it for years. It's a melding of information, purpose, and being on the cutting edge of innovation.

I can't imagine being a dean without informatics expertise. And, of course, data. We need to know what is going on internally. We need to be wise stewards of resources before we invest the precious resource of people, especially given a nursing faculty shortage. We do not go blind into the night. With information, deep conversations grow and are followed by purpose-filled action.

Some financial decisions make accounting look good. Some make a leader look good. However, what matters most is making long-term decisions instead of prioritizing short-term wins—continually acting for the good of the organization rather than self. I am an instigator,

a tool; we are the result.

As leaders, all of us need to be ready to leave the position we're in every day we're in it. I've thought and lived that way for my entire career. When I wake up each day, I commit myself to fully engage. And I will make the best decisions for the school that my awareness supports. If something else comes before the best decision for the school, then that's the day I should leave. It's one way I continuously do an internal check on myself: am I being objective, advocating for the school and the needs of this unique community?

That doesn't mean I live partially committed. It's precisely the opposite. By keeping the purpose in mind, I'm all in. I constantly hold myself accountable for a school that will one day be in another dean's hands. What legacy am I helping create? From day one, I have committed to doing everything I can so the next dean inherits a school that's optimistic, high functioning, has sustainable finances and resources, and most significantly is a community, a WE ARE.

WHAT IF? KEEP LISTENING

Several years ago, I joined some friends on a moderately challenging hike. It was hotter than usual, and the going was steep. Hill after hill, no breeze, sun blazing; it was tough. When reaching the top of anything, there's jubilation. A feeling of accomplishment and a buzz felt at meeting one's goals. I was feeling like this. I'd done the work, and I made it to the top. And then a large bus came along. It wound its way up the hills and stopped at the top in front of an ice cream shop. The passengers disembarked and paraded into the shop for some ice cream. I felt a bit demoralized when I had to follow them in, and my choice of ice cream, fresh lemon, was all gone. I thought I deserved this ice cream and I had worked for it. I know it's silly, the people on the bus who rode to the top and casually went in and feasted on the same winnings that I had fought so hard for didn't seem right. Working hard for anything deserves some winnings. However, it doesn't always happen. We don't all start at the same place, and we're not all given the same road to success, and sometimes people don't like the way you do it. I had worked hard for my job. During my first two years as dean of the nursing school, our faculty and staff implemented all of the recommendations for change that had been identified. I'd been hired to make a difference, and I had. I'd climbed the hills and I wanted my ice cream.

After five more years in the position, I experienced a human resource challenge. While we were clearly transformational in our work, this incident created distrust and anger. There was disappointment in me. Some of the faculty wanted me out.

In higher education, faculty can request a vote of no confidence to remove a leader. Seven years into my tenure as dean, several faculty members decided it was my time to go.

I was climbing the mountain I had committed to. The challenges of so many changes and perhaps rocking the status quo had created waves. How was I to cope?

While most people had rallied around the transformations that grew out of the intense collaboration we had put into place, a few dissented.

Five years after my arrival, the National Institutes of Health (NIH) announced it would focus significant funding on sixty research sites across the United States. In addition to building an extensive national infrastructure dedicated to healthcare innovation, the Clinical and Translational Science Award program (CTSA) would drive collaboration by requiring funded recipients to share data, disseminate their findings, and partner with other organizations. For the University of Minnesota, the program would accelerate School of Nursing partnerships with other CTSA participants, including the Mayo Clinic, healthcare systems, and businesses that wanted to advance collaborative research or implement discoveries.

The University of Minnesota had competed for funding in four rounds and fallen short. We readied our proposal and learned that biomedical informatics needed to be accelerated for us to compete for funding.

My informatics background was a key reason the School of Nursing had chosen me to be dean. My appointment as the first nursing dean in the world recognized as a Fellow in the American College of Medical Informatics (FACMI) made a statement nationally and internationally.

The university asked if I would be willing to leave the deanship to lead the biomedical informatics component. While I wasn't willing to leave the deanship, I would consider assuming both roles. Our executive vice president for the Academic Health Center, Frank Cerra, led discussions with the School of Nursing faculty and staff to explain why I might be able to assume two full-time positions. I would only do it with the support of the school. The enthusiasm was tremendous, and the go-ahead was immediate. The reasons were many:

- My participation would increase the visibility of the School of Nursing at the university.
- Success would mean joining a consortium of sixty top large research sites.
- Awarding the grant would secure the largest grant in university history.

I negotiated administrative support and what I thought I needed to do both jobs. I also assumed interim directorship of the University's Academic Health Center's Institute for Health Informatics. These three appointments were synergistic. I loved the work and felt that this was part of my calling.

Prevailing leadership wisdom says a leader's first year is an opening to make sweeping changes. After that, the goodwill of a honeymoon year is over. I had pushed the limit for close to five years and I felt we could continue this accelerated change rate. While most faculty and staff welcomed change, a small group reacted with shock and resistance.

And the resistance became deeply challenging personally and professionally.

How does one respond to opposition?

It was a dramatic turnaround. To go from the feeling of appreciation and acceptance to being shunned and told to go. The experience filled me with doubt and I wasn't sure how to address the situation. One day the executive vice president and provost of the university came to our all-school meeting with flowers to say how proud he was of our success in winning the enormous CTSA grant. Then, within a year, he was back to sort out issues with those who didn't like my style and were looking for a change. This was an unexpected turn of events for me and was a challenge I hadn't foreseen.

I gave my national dean's Board of Visitors as much information as I could share. This group of highly talented leaders committed to working with me through these difficulties. As individuals and as a group, they said, "Connie, now you've been baptized. Until you face this as an executive, you don't realize it happens to everyone. We are here to support you." That advice carried me through.

From the time I enrolled in school as a child, there was one stable bit of knowledge in my life. It was my confidence in being successful in the academic environment. I continued completing a degree even when my husband abandoned me and my son. By the time this opposition as a dean had struck, I had established myself well enough to support my own family, friends, and others. This experience was part of my essence. Knowing how this past incident would help me in this exploit had never entered my mind. I was using it now.

Suddenly, I wasn't in control. I realized that my performance would not guarantee professional security and that my academic expertise was insufficient to secure my position.

We held discussions with the executive vice president and brought in outside facilitators and consultants as guides. I patiently listened. I wanted to learn and understand with humility.

Over time I grew thankful for this experience and these meetings.

I realized two things. First, we were still undergoing a massive transformation; and second, all these issues, thoughts, and feelings needed to come out, to surface, and to be expressed. Most were historical experiences (decades old). Like in any relationship, anger festering inside will erode the relationship. It needs to surface. So, the meetings were a massive catharsis.

As I listened, I recognized that a few complaints were about me. Issues I needed to address. While those stung, it was also important to hear them and discern how I would address them. Much of the anger related to activities that happened long before I came to the university. Some of it was thirty years old. Nevertheless, it needed to be aired, so I continued to listen. There were also instances when I felt "thrown under the bus" for the sake of the larger organization, and that hurt. And I learned as well. I learned that an organization determines what is worth clarifying when issues are brought to the surface and dealt with. If not brought forward, negativity and unrest perpetuate, and growth is stunted.

People wondered why I didn't cry or scream. They asked me how I could sit there and be present. I wasn't only sitting. I was listening. I was absorbing, and I was learning.

I was given a great gift. Ultimately, I could explain that all the challenges, experiences, and issues were necessary for me to know. I learned about the history and understandings of the people I work with daily. I was hearing information and recognizing the baggage that they had been carrying for years. I worked hard, not taking it personally. I needed to stay the course and I needed to keep listening.

It takes hard work to get to the top and yet that place up there can get lonely. Sometimes we are attacked from below, sometimes we are sideswiped, and sometimes we are shot down. Going through this undulating phase of flowers and praise to the disappointing realization that people wanted me out was hurtful, humbling, and eventually went from disjointed chaos to resolution. I did "get my ice-cream", yet it wasn't easy. Synergy and the ongoing goal of a bigger picture got us through. Listening with love was added to my leading with love philosophy. Asking questions, listening to the answers and not attacking, not only got me through the ordeal, it gave me the newfound stamina to keep climbing.

Longfellow wrote: "If we could read the secret history of our enemies, we should find in each one's life sorrow and suffering enough to disarm all our hostility."

THE FREEDOM TO THINK: INNOVATION

When I was young, I had frequent conversations with our church's pastor. Even as an eight-year-old, the weekly Sunday school and sermons often left me with more questions than answers. I don't understand, I'd say to him; this doesn't make sense and certainly doesn't add up.

So I'm very aware that since childhood I have had a strong bent towards endless questions. I couldn't accept answers that didn't make sense both to my head and my heart.

From early on, I liked venturing out and seeing possibilities. Welcoming challenges. Breaking barriers. This might not sound like an introvert's attitude. It has two sides, like I believe we all do. I have a strong sense of conformity. I like a welcoming structure and concrete policies. As a dean and in the role and function needed in higher education, we as leaders have required many years of preparation and experience, obtaining degrees, gaining organizational insights, and becoming increasingly versed in bureaucratic systems. These "rules" have given me comfort and keep me safe. They pave the roads. The questioning side of my behavior and the venturing out part of my personality are what drive me forward with curiosity and creativity. It's the kind of car I drive on that road.

T.S. Eliot said: "It's not wise to violate rules until you know how to observe them." And that's one of the reasons I value my structured upbringing, study and educational practices, work ethic, and the journey as a dean. I now find myself drawn to expanding beyond the traditional. I choose less traveled routes. I chart innovative new paths.

I do not set out to break the rules for the sake of breaking the rules. I feel my way forward by asking questions.

Organizational practices often control people by limiting their vision and impairing their consideration of the world of options between being rule-bound and running loose with few to no controls. The best rules, guidelines, and standards aren't imposed from above. They grow out of our relationships and interconnections and keep us working in the same direction.

So how could breaking norms propel you toward your goals? Another worthy question.

When I arrived at the nursing school, faculty and staff had already established a lofty goal to rank among the nation's top ten NIH nursing schools. At the time, the school wasn't positioned firmly to meet such a goal. It was nevertheless a tremendous goal, and we stayed focused on the ranking and on what the order represented. Three years ago, the University of Minnesota School of Nursing rose to its goal and was rated tenth in the nation. We didn't become the best in a class by doing what we had always done, nor by copying what other schools were doing. We've become known for edgy thinking, innovation, and many other firsts.

We created a Doctor of Nursing Practice (DNP), one of the first in the nation and now the largest in the country. This was an initiative to create nurse practitioners demonstrating excellence in practice, a complement to the research degree of PhD.

We further distinguished our offers by launching twelve specialties. We were the first in the nation to offer DNPs in nursing informatics, integrative health and healing, nurse anesthesia, and health innovation and leadership.

Years after these initiatives launched, the American Association of Colleges of Nursing (AACN) recognized that the DNP degree encompasses all these specialties.

The DNP degree fits perfectly. It proves how adaptive we've become and how we have learned to think outside the box. We extended the boundaries of the norms, fostered the importance of the context of care, and we fostered diverse expertise. We pushed further and became better. We moved up to the top of the mountain, and we didn't do it by riding a bus.

Our school has always admitted non-nurses to our PhD program. Some ask, "Can non-nurses conceptualize and do nursing research?" We recognize the difference between practicing as a nurse and studying nurses and nursing. Our school has great numbers of faculty who are excellent computer scientists, engineers, and social scientists. And even though these faculty and staff are not licensed nurses, we are all nursing. If you met these unlicensed persons, you would likely not realize they weren't nurses unless you checked their resumes. When others shut out innovative leaders, we opened doors and welcomed them.

We established a clinical track for faculty that provides continuity with tenure-track academics. Historically, tenured faculty focused on research and enjoyed benefits not available to professors dedicated to equipping nurses for clinical practice. We recognized that the University of Minnesota rule was that only tenured faculty could be designated as emeritus upon retirement. This title provides a lifelong welcome in the university community. No equivalent was available to clinical faculty. So, within our school we created an "ad honorem" title for clinical track retirees. Clinical track faculty who meet specific criteria, which they helped codevelop, were honored with the same rights and responsibilities as the emeritus designation in the school. We have used our freedom to think, and it has paid off.

We were the first in the nation to have a Director of Planetary Health. As the world began to acknowledge climate change and challenges to the sustainability of life on earth, we had the foresight to invest in leadership in this area of high importance.

Of course, in any field there is a tendency to watch what competitors are doing. Our goal has been to maintain awareness of what others are doing and then go beyond. We celebrate the successes of others, and then use our own experience and imagination to foster our goals. When we hear about a significant win from another institution, we listen, we compliment their efforts, and then we continue to focus on our direction. As we continue to respect the evolution of change among us, we know that nothing is impossible.

When something doesn't work, we change course. Nothing is a failure, because we always learn from it. It's the beginning of our next big thing. What did we learn? How can we use this? How do we move on? It's more than handing out gold stars for achievement; it's a continual breath. It's an innovative live experiment meant to transform. Asking questions and following rules; breaking them as well, we ride on the edge.

Richard Rohr wrote: "prophets, by their very nature, cannot be at the center of any social structure. They cannot be full insiders, but they cannot throw rocks from outside either." Rather, they are "on the edge of the inside." They must be educated inside the system, knowing and living the rules, before they can critique what is non-essential or unimportant. Jesus did this masterfully, Martin Luther King taught this in the United States, Gandhi taught British-occupied India, and Nelson Mandela led South Africa. We learn from the best.

TRANSPARENCY

The quiet felt peaceful. It was also a bit scary. The white noise we get so used to had all stopped. No more blinking, beeping, or pumping. I was with a patient in a room full of people where everyone was doing their part. Working on my own tasks, I noticed there were now only four of us in the room. Then three of us. Then I was alone with the patient. The quiet was even stronger, and now I knew what that meant.

He was still alert. The machines had stopped beating; his heart still pumped. I looked away from the charts, I adjusted my belt, and stood still. I was looking into his eyes, and he looked straight back into mine. They say the eyes are the doorway to the soul. I started to understand this. I can still feel our connection. As if we're together right now. It was so real. There was no judgment, no lessons or prompting or preaching or regretting. Not even any crying. He looked deeply at me. I knew that he could still feel the blood flowing. And then he asked me, "Am I dying?"

In this most intimate moment, time is suspended. Nothing else matters. I reminded myself to keep breathing, and in that moment of human connectedness, I said, "Yes." I am here with you, and yes. I didn't need to explain. He already knew. I needed to answer his call to be truthful, to take his last breath in peace. He knew he was dying.

And then he was gone. I didn't feel scared now. I felt honored. It was a gift to share this last moment. To look into someone's eyes in the last moments of their life and to see and feel that acceptance made me so grateful that I was a nurse. We had nursed him. I had nursed him. I found new meaning in this word "nurse." I must nurse myself and nurse my friends and nurse this incredible world we are part of. I covered him and left the room.

Transparency is a big word and it's especially important today. What does it mean to you? What does it mean to your organization? I am a person who says whatever is on my mind. I tell colleagues and friends that I will always speak the truth, even if it hurts. Others aren't so ready to share their thoughts. Life experiences might have taught them that speaking up isn't safe. Another person might say that they can't talk right now. There's something they need to digest. Something was said that they needed to think over and talk about later.

Some of my most agonizing situations have involved waiting for others to speak freely. I'm not anxious about what someone might tell me. Whatever they have to say, I listen. The most challenging part is waiting; that is giving up control.

In the interim, as people digest a situation to figure out what they think and feel, a relationship hangs in the balance. A connection that matters a lot. The suspense and uncertainty can be difficult to the point of bringing out a feeling of brokenness and despair. It can be an achy sensation of physical hurt, like every cell in your body hurts, both emotional and physical. Leaders often insist on dictating the timing and outcome of conversations. However, making space for others and considering their opinions is often the only way for transparency to happen for everyone.

Transparency is being open. It frees the path for flowing communication. It implies accountability.

Transparency includes inviting others to speak. And it sometimes needs the willingness to hold our words until others feel ready to engage in conversation.

Difficult conversations occur. In any group or organization, things don't all go the way all members want them to go. Meeting with a faculty member to inform them that their peer group didn't support a promotion is devastating news. People want to leave. To hide.

We can talk it through. I can point out all the specifics of what was accomplished. I can remind people that they are magnificent. I can ask if they are willing to try again. I can convey support.

A few days after I had one of these experiences, I received a note: "Connie, I want to thank you. That was the most caring, supportive conversation in the most difficult circumstance. And yes, let's work together." I am sharing this because of the writer's open-hearted maturity. Not because of my response. I will indeed enjoy working with this person further.

Few of our transparent moments concern literal life or death. As time stands still, we can't underestimate the significance of our every step, every word, and every micro action.

Transparency helps foster trust and collaboration. Open and honest communication is shared and is accessible to all. This leads to better decision making and a higher standard in patient care. We hear the tale of the left foot not knowing where the right foot is going. Many institutions, and especially government agencies and institutes of higher education, work in a separatist type of environment. This creates misunderstandings and conflicts, and puts everyone on a different page. Working together promotes accountability, responsibility and standards that work for everyone. This kind of transparent atmosphere improves outcomes for a better work environment and for a better patient outcome.

Because I am a proponent of oneness, I believe that we are all interconnected. We are part of a larger whole. When this is applied in a nursing workplace or a university program, it creates unity. A shared purpose evolves. Sharing—I cannot say it enough. Sharing information, data, knowledge, creates a sense of collaboration. More than a sense, a reality. Oneness and transparency work together. Joy is an outcome. The positive, supportive environment created through transparency is another example of leading with love. Everyone is involved, everyone wins.

PANDEMIC, CHALLENGES, LIFE

Shame on me, said a friend of mine who lives in England. Shame on me. When I asked her what she meant by that, she told me about her neighbor Kim. Kim's husband had died a few years ago and so she now lived alone. There were always sounds coming from her garden. Sweeping the walk, raking away the fallen rhododendron petals, stacking up the twigs fallen from the copper beech and the peaceful hum of work in the garden. Kim seemed ok, said my friend. And then the pandemic hit. Everyone was to be isolated so my friend decided that she could create a bubble and include Kim. She shopped for her once a week and she had her over for dinner every night during the first eight weeks of COVID. She didn't think this was a big deal, it was being neighborly. Then Kim started saying how happy she was. How lucky that she shared dinner with three or four other people every night, that she had daily comradery, care, friendship. She said that COVID was the best thing that had ever happened to her. They played Jenga and croquet and put together crossword puzzles. And this is why my friend was unhappy with herself. How had she not noticed how lonely Kim had been? Why didn't she think about her having dinner alone every night? Why did it take a catastrophe, a pandemic, to have Kim over for dinner?

And that is the gist of her story. Don't wait for a disaster. Don't wait until loneliness takes a person down. Don't wait to be asked or approached or begged. Just do it. Listen to your neighbors and the needy. Listen with love. Step out of your narrow doorway and open up your arms. It took COVID to get my friend to do this. Hopefully you won't wait so long.

So how does this work in an institution? In a university? This is an example of an individual who found a way out of loneliness into a vibrant relationship. Kim was brought into a solution. Into a community. Into a safe place. And this has to happen at a bigger level as well. Instead of going it alone and with fear, we need to band together and go forward with conviction.

The arrival of SARS-CoV-2 was a double heartache for the University of Minnesota School of Nursing. The challenges of the COVID pandemic to colleges and universities put into question the viability of many institutions. And as a School of Nursing with students from undergraduates to doctoral candidates, we found ourselves equipping them to grapple with the most significant public health crisis of our lifetime.

A natural human reaction is to pull the covers over our heads, hide, hibernate, and pretend it's not real. Wake me up when this is over. We who have a plan, a direction and are committed to our mission follow one of our core principles. When we sense we fear something, we run toward the challenge.

The world was about six months into COVID when our executive team of seven people met on Zoom, a habit we repeated weekly, sometimes daily. I said to the group, "Okay, we need to pause. Please look at each of us on this screen. Imagine what tomorrow would be like if one or more of us is not here."

Silence. In that silence, we knew that hospitalization and death were weaving their way through each one of our hearts and our heads, beyond the numbers reported in the news, beyond our families and friends and nursing colleagues. In this critical moment we each needed to be fully open. No topic was off-limits. Through this shared experience, we affirmed the preciousness of each person and our shared gratitude for their presence. We expressed our individual and group vulnerability. We created the transparency that said, "If not me, then who steps in?"

As an executive team, we surrendered. Not to fear, not to the impulse to immediately attempt to fix problems we barely understood, least of all to defeat. Instead, we erased our assumptions. We embraced being in the moment. We determined that the process of discovery is what really matters—the vulnerability of each one of us and the school. And we allowed solutions to emerge.

We discussed contingency plans in case tomorrow one of us wasn't present or if one of us succumbed to COVID and died. We developed backup plans for each of us and every vital function of the school. We discussed solvency. When the university asked us to model a ten percent budget cut, we profiled what our budget would look like at a fifty percent cut. We went further than the university asked to get a sense of what a radically revamped school could be.

I was able to share with the executive team that I had already spoken to the dean of the university's College of Pharmacy. We would partner through this crisis with contingency leadership backup in each of our environments. People in Pharmacy and our School of Nursing people all knew we had a plan.

Our discussions of worst-case cuts to our program weren't easy. When we contemplated any of us being in the ICU or dying, we cried. Our frank conversations brought home the challenges we faced. This is real. We're not immune. Let's deal with it.

As our conversations unfolded, the solutions weren't mine. Solutions emerged from our interactions and thinking together—another example of the oneness of our team.

When our executive team members returned to their units, each reminded staff and faculty about how we had worked together through these challenges. We could share with the faculty and staff that we had planned for the worst and continued to hope for the best.

As hard as it might be to hear or imagine, we made ourselves repeat this challenging exercise at unit levels. Every leader reminded their team to pause. If we are not here tomorrow, how would we continue what we have built?

We faced the challenge, remained non-fear based, and now had backup plans. The exercise was meant to quiet our inner selves and free us to get back to action.

As time unfolded, our school kept students engaged. We graduated everybody. We remained financially viable. And when we could have gone into the winter season of hibernation and despair, we experienced a spring of renewal and a summer of growth.

Living in denial is deadening. Embracing challenges, planning thoroughly, and testing solutions diminishes fear and leaves no place for rejection.

As leaders, we can create an atmosphere of calm. People are looking for safety, and we can only partially ensure this. Feeling fear and going beyond it gives people confidence. By planning and accepting the problems, we helped move away from upheaval, chaos, and drama, and towards a smooth flow and outcome.

I hope that I lead as I live. When I fear something personally, I imagine it and most times go after it. I like skydiving. I enjoy parasailing. I became a pilot. None of these activities are possible if I let fear rule me. When I sense fear, I let it in. Yes, much of this did grow from my early experience with marriage—what I feared the most actually happened. I touch it and get to know what it feels like. I become comfortable with it and then learn to go beyond it so that when I ask myself if I can actually do something, I almost always answer yes.

As leaders, we do everything we can to create safety for our loved ones, our organizations, and our world. Nursing is all about creating safety for patients, families, and communities. Being a dean involves building layers of safety and security within an academic institution.

As leaders, it takes courage to stay alert to challenges, safeguard information, and absorb uncertainty and stress as we work through challenges with our team. Frequently we must discern where, when, how, and with whom we share details. As our minds wander to what can happen and we feel caught up in dramatic scenarios, we titrate needs to stay within a tight circle of leaders to absorb uncertainty and stress within the organization.

At the right time, we disseminate accurate information. It's easy for people in charge to escalate a situation, make it clear that they're handling everything, and expand on the million hours a week they spend on this. "I've got this," they say when really, it's got them. Their ego has taken over, and things are getting out of control.

I said "people in charge" because that is quite different from being a leader. It's possible to go to the highest level, even the president of the United States, and be in charge, and yet not necessarily be a leader. An alternative script is when the leader says, "We are facing a challenge. We will look hard at it, learn from it, and partner to solve it. We will continue to monitor the situation and share information as we can. If we work together, we will get through this." These are the words of a leader. Kim had neighbors who helped her out of a lonely rut. We have a team, a university, a vibrant working entity. We too have pulled out of that rut and persevered. Going it alone has no place in a leading with love world.

RECKONING

On May 25, 2020, a police officer knelt on George Floyd for eight minutes and forty-six seconds. George Floyd died, and the world erupted. As a nursing school in the Minneapolis and St. Paul area, we were only five miles from the site of this violence. We were not only experiencing the depths of COVID; we were also at the epicenter of reactions to the murder of George Floyd. The event laid bare the rampant racial injustice in our city, country, and world. The School of Nursing immediately committed to owning our part of discrimination. What does that mean?

I didn't think that I was prejudiced when I asked a member of our school staff to be my internal consultant. We both wanted a conversation about the recent events. I assumed my associate, Donald, would teach me while I listened. What I discovered was his unbelievable discernment and willingness to address issues. And he wanted to hear. He had questions for me that seemed simple and yet bold, intimate, and enlightening. He asked me when I first knew a black person. My experiences were minimal growing up in a rural farming area in northeast Iowa. I remember seeing the first black person in my teens when a family in our area adopted a young boy.

Donald went on to tell me that like many people, his dream had been to not see color; unfortunately, he learned that this was not reality. I learned that when people say to him, "I don't see color," it hurts him. "It disregards me" he said. We're at a stage in our society's evolution where we recognize that color is essential. I learned from him that intentions don't matter; impact does. Diversity, equity and inclusion training in companies, schools, and organizations today focus on impact over intent. One might not have intended to cause harm, yet did. These were lessons I needed to learn. Carlos A. Rodriguez, founder of The Happy Non-Profit, writes:

> "I see no color" is not the goal.
> "I see your color, and I honor you. I value your input. I will be educated about your lived experiences. I will work against the racism that harms you. You are beautiful.
> Tell me how to do better."
> ... That's the goal.

A reckoning is an accounting for things done or not done. By its nature, it is usually an instance when someone else tells you that you've fallen short. Having a reckoning can mean you are going to hold someone accountable. My reckoning with prejudice took me by surprise. It was my assumptions, my inexperience, and yes, my naïvety that held me responsible for an inherent type of prejudice. George Floyd, the person, is gone; what he left us is more significant than we might have imagined. It has opened us up to the possibility that we might be wrong. That we don't know everything. That we do indeed hold prejudices. One of the gifts from the death of George Floyd is that space has opened to see the hidden, to hear stories that were silent until now, to talk about the unacceptable, and commit to doing better.

As a school, we strive to achieve unwavering growth in our commitment to inclusivity, diversity, and equity. We together affirm that we have had enough talk. We need to act. We need to make proactive plans that permeate all aspects of our school. We need to address the needs and relationships of our minorities. We need to ask them, not assume. We must set an example in our offices, classrooms, the school, and beyond. To not be seen, to not be valued, to not be heard—this is a wrong of society, and we will rectify, apologize, and act upon this tragedy. And in our school, we did that.

Rosa Parks said, "To bring about change, you must not be afraid to take the first step. We will fail when we fail to try." She was talking about her first steps and those of her fellow activists. We need to take those steps. It is our turn to be activists. Let us not wait any longer.

In our 114-year-old School of Nursing, we noted our core founding principles of educating nurses articulated by our founder Richard Olding Beard: the focus of not only "training" them as was the practice elsewhere, while recognizing the worth of human life, conserving human health, and furthering social justice.

We recognize that the healthcare system is meant to protect and heal people and yet it has supported structures of racism that have contributed to ongoing trauma and health inequities. We acknowledge that the Twin Cities campus of the University of Minnesota is built on the traditional homeland of the Dakota People, the traditional stewards of this land. We also acknowledge the violence of colonialism and ongoing racism toward indigenous people. Our chief administrative officer and director of human resources support and execute the school's equity salary adjustments for faculty and staff. Their expertise ensures our school can maintain our commitment to the AACN benchmarks for competitive faculty salaries.

Our school's inclusivity, diversity, and equity committee regularly call us back to our intention to be a welcoming, sensitive, and inclusive community. They help us examine implicit and explicit bias. They lead us in transcending gaps and advancing mutual respect, dignity, and safety for all.

My reaction to these points is first, I am grateful for our progress. For the past seven years, the School of Nursing has been recognized nationally as a recipient of the higher education excellence in diversity award, which recognizes colleges and universities that demonstrate an outstanding commitment to diversity and inclusion.

And second, I see so much more to do. In our Twin Cities and beyond, the problems of racism go on and on. We learn daily about violence in word, deed, and spirit. This must be addressed and recognized. The institutionalized racism that permeates all of society needs to end. We cannot use statements like "the past is the past," or "I'm not a racist any more." We must act. There is a pain that is deep in our souls. Time alone solves little. Thoughts and prayers aren't enough. We must act.

As leaders, our job is to believe the people who tell us they have suffered wrong and to invest in doing what it takes to correct past and present injustices. There's nowhere better to start than within our organizations. These need to be places where we can welcome the rich diversity of experiences and backgrounds our team members bring and lean in to all they can teach us.

I am sad that our university denied a young black woman student, Francis McHie, admission without good reason. She graduated from Minneapolis South High School in 1929. She applied to the nursing school at the University of Minnesota and was denied admission because of her color. Being a strong and driven woman, she went to the state legislature and secured admission. She was the first black woman to graduate from the school in 1932. She also earned her BS degree from the School of Education. She was the first black employee of the Minneapolis General Hospital as supervisor of the outpatient clinic. She was the first black person to work with the Visiting Nurses Association in New Orleans. And she was one of the twelve nurses who broke the color barrier at Herman Kiefer Hospital in Detroit. Francis McHie served as associate professor and assistant to the director of the School of Nursing at Tuskegee Institute and Nashville's Meharry Medical College and DON for their Hubbard Hospital. She was a woman who didn't take no for an answer, who fought for what she deserved and used what she learned to lead the way for others.

Years later, I received a visit from her nephew, who asked me if I knew who he was. Did I know the story of his aunt?

I knew the story, and I verbally apologized. Private apologies for such a public act are inadequate. I publicly invited him to a large student body meeting, apologized, and committed to additional school actions. Talk is not enough. Later in the year, this man received the Richard Olding Beard Award to thank him for speaking up, supporting action, and living the Beard principles. He started a scholarship fund for nursing students in honor of his aunt.

Our efforts can't stop until our eyes are larger and we see beyond the past. We must engage in the radical connectedness of leading with love. We need to be part of the creation of One World. A world where racism no longer exists, where it is replaced with One Humanity, love.

Darkness cannot drive out darkness; only light can do that.
Hate cannot drive out hate; only love can do that.

Martin Luther King Jr.

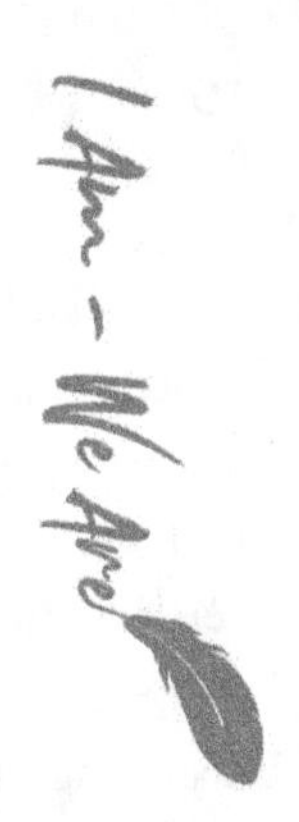

VULNERABILITY

COVID was the last thing on my mind when my brother Clark and his husband arrived at my home for a weekend visit in April 2021.

Vaccines were now available, and yet there were still many unknowns. I was living a very secluded life. Although many people were still in denial, I was collecting my mail fully masked. I went to school at night or on weekends when nobody was present. When I went out for essentials, I was always masked and maintained a distance from others. When my brother arrived, I mentioned that I was tired. He and his partner immediately sensed things weren't as good as I related. They suggested I get checked for COVID; I wasn't interested. After all, I'd been practicing excellent protocol, and it was highly unlikely.

Before returning home to Iowa on Monday, Clark insisted on taking me to the emergency room. As I readied to leave my condo, I discovered I was much weaker than I had thought and needed help to the elevator. Within less than half an hour after arriving at the ER, a nurse announced that I had COVID. I needed to be admitted to intensive care. I still had difficulty believing it because I had no apparent symptoms. I did feel exhausted yet I had no temperature and no loss of taste or smell.

In the ICU, I received oxygen plus IV meds. I was repeatedly asked for permission to be intubated. "I've already answered that," I'd say. "No, if I get to that stage, then we will talk." I reminded myself that I was an experienced ICU nurse.

I settled into the bed, resting and concentrating on breathing. For six days, I meditated around the clock. I was focused on integrating traditional Western medicine and working with a healer knowledgeable in Eastern healthcare methods. I had my cell phone and computer by my side. I felt no pain. In this quiet, I was enveloped in perfect peace.

Periodically, nurses and medical personnel quietly came in to complete assessments and treatments. I dealt with the facts and asked a few questions. What is my oxygen saturation? What medications are you giving me? What's the drip rate of the intravenous infusions? My blood pressure? Pulse? These are all questions that any nurse would want to know.

When my brother left me in the ER to park the car, we separated without knowing we wouldn't see each other again that day. No goodbyes or anything. No one could enter the room except for a few hospital staff. I couldn't leave. My physical world became very small. My nurse practitioner brought me bottled water and assorted power sources. I was connected by phone and computer to the world. My office knew I was sick. They had no idea I was in the ICU three blocks away.

I was not lying in fear. I wasn't worried. I didn't think of anyone or anything except being present in the focused moment. I had managed to find a flow with my situation. I had an illness, accepted it, and treated it with the wholeness I felt. It's the difference between floating on a tumultuous sea versus fighting with the waves. I would be all right.

As my brother was the one who dropped me off at the hospital, it was he who drove three hours back to Minneapolis to settle me back home. I was told that someone should stay with me. This idea got pushed to the side of my mind; I have always assumed that I can handle things independently. Clark set me up with groceries, and I told him everything would be fine. I gave him my deepest thanks and promised to stay in touch.

And so it was with complete oblivion that I was bowled over by a flood of anguish, hurt, and disappointment.

I had been home for only a few hours when I began hearing about the issues I had created. Almost every member of my family was angry, hurt, and felt disrespected. And so were my friends. And so were my supposedly close fellow university team members.

I began hearing people say, "I thought we were close. I don't know if I can trust you again. I had no idea how sick you were. Why didn't you let me know so I could help? Who did get a call? Why not me? Why did you leave me out?" Everyone wondered why I hadn't used my phone to communicate with them. I could say I was concentrating on breathing, which would be accurate, although it was not helpful.

My brother was supposed to be the go-between. He and the caregivers were to pass on information to my son and family. Clark shared the information he had, and it wasn't much. My very busy caretakers gave minimal information, which was extremely worrying to my family. The lack of information created distress and deep anguish among the people who wanted to know what was happening. When we leave people with unknowns, they will fill in the blanks, and the filler is often so much worse than what's actual.

I had inadvertently exposed Clark and Christopher to COVID during their weekend stay. The fact that COVID never entered my mind and I had no usual symptoms did not matter. Me trying to go it alone was not helping anyone. While I thought I was protecting others by handling things myself, those same "others" felt hurt, disrespected, and at a loss of what kind of mother, daughter, sister, friend, or colleague I was.

It wasn't clear to me right away. I'd been in my own world, and it took me time to realize that my world was not only about me and my independence. Did I take this too far? Did I hold on to myself in a way that was selfish? Is it okay to be selfish? It was all about me at this time and it took the response of others to pull me out of that inner self and come back to the world of WE. I had put my own privacy and control above everyone else. I am a private person and I believe that everyone has the right to privacy. If I truly believe in community, if I believe in a oneness that is essential to this world, then I need to be more inclusive. Going it alone is not an option.

Yet I had created anger and disappointment, and it needed some rectification. I wrote a letter to my mom, my son and his wife, and my brothers and sisters. I apologized. I shared all of the facts of which I was aware. I expressed my gratitude for them being in my life and shared what I had learned through my mistakes and how I was going to change.

Sometimes we can step out of our bodies. We can look upon ourselves and see this content person, sick person, or whatever, and we see the "me." I forgot to look down at the whole. That I am part of something much bigger than myself. I realized I almost died. How blessed was I that my brother insisted on taking me to the hospital? That insistence was the beginning of my physical recovery and also the beginning of another starting point. My recovery was one small part of the whole.

I read somewhere that being wrong feels exactly the same as being right until we find out we were wrong. I looked at the hurt that everyone had experienced. I looked at my inability to discern my own health. I looked at the importance of communication, in my job and also personally. I was sorry—an achingly heartfelt sorry.

I hadn't let them in, and through this experience, I had another growth spurt and am grateful for how forgiving my friends and family have been.

I now realize that my close call with COVID had changed my leadership style and interaction with family, friends, and colleagues. It created a willingness to share my own needs and a tenderness in relating to people.

Before others pointed out the difficulties I had created, I perceived myself as an open sharer and good listener. This bold painful meeting with my vulnerability has fostered a greater sensitivity. My ability to admit my needs defines the degree to which I can be honest, trustworthy, and compassionate with others. I never realized how strong one could be when practicing transparency and gentleness. Letting oneself be vulnerable is a sign of strength. My lack of sharing and my lack of inclusiveness hurt my circle of family and friends and me. I must have forgotten that we call it a circle.

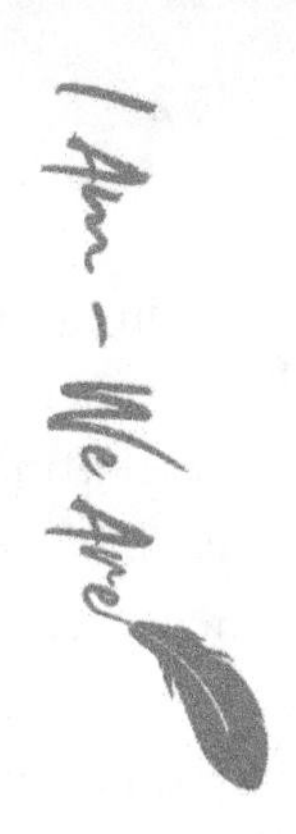

HUMANS

The Berlin Wall stood for twenty-eight years before it came down after only two months of public protests.

In 1963, 200,000 demonstrators peacefully gathered at the Lincoln Memorial to hear Martin Luther King's historic "I have a Dream" speech. President Kennedy was pressured to improve civil rights legislation. Nelson Mandela's ANC party organized anti-apartheid days called "stay at home." Stay-at-home days contributed to the eventual abolition of apartheid. Gandhi went on a Salt March, a twenty-four-day journey to collect his salt, which was illegal under British law. It turned the tide, and India eventually broke from British rule.

We could fill a book with these types of examples. Change is what makes us grow. Accepting human growth is being vulnerable and vulnerability allows change. Letting transparency bring us closer together helps achieve change within a group. Working together creates a form of identity. And identity drives our goals as a member of a group, a gang, a community, or even a change.

Society holds on to what it knows, what it deems to be safe. The individual and the group swim against the current that brings about change. And this doesn't happen quickly. The establishment can drown an idea. It will push and push, trying to hold on to "what's always been."

The women's rights movement is an example. Equal rights started to develop in the United States because women learned to read and write in North America earlier than in most European countries. When a person can read and write, they can think for themselves. And hence, question how society works. These first dissenters focused on abolishing slavery and gaining women's right to vote. The tenacity and unfailing energy these women incorporated into the fight for our future is too often forgotten and taken for granted. I may have had few choices of what field to go into when I began my higher education, however, those choices resulted from women who came before me. My double major in nursing and mathematics was fully welcomed by my fellow mathematics students, most of whom were men. As I entered the field of informatics, I partnered professionally with computer scientists and engineers. This was a man's world, and I was lucky that my colleagues were magnificent.

Some parts of the world move ahead quickly and other parts lag. Saudi Arabian women only recently got the vote and the right to drive. I have been fortunate to work in Iceland, where I've taught, conducted scholarship, and addressed various initiatives for over twenty years. Iceland has had a woman as president or prime minister for twenty of the last thirty-six years. Vigdis Finnbogadottir, an Icelandic politician who served from 1980 to 1996, was Iceland's fourth president and the world's first woman president. In Iceland, a female leader has become the norm.

As a woman and a leader, I am aware of the difficulties I encounter despite the growth we've had. I also take the responsibility to continue this positive direction that those before me have made happen. I want to be a role model to both men and women. Men, too, have had difficult times in "being who they are," and in nursing, this is especially true. Men who don't fit the social norms of masculinity can struggle. I see the most beautiful, gentle, incredible men as nurses, yet these "soft" characteristics can often be cast as weak. What a colossal mistake that is.

Some of the points I try to emphasize regarding gender in my leadership role are:

- We celebrate our wholeness, recognizing that each of us has masculine and feminine characteristics.
- We put aside assumptions and judgments about what an individual might think, say, or do because of gender.
- We invite people out of the shadows and veils, knowing that no one is less or more than because of gender.
- We welcome people to speak for themselves, respecting their insights.

In the environment following the U.S. Supreme Court striking down Roe v. Wade, I watched men shut out women's voices and women shutting out what men might say about how abortion impacts them.

When we come together as equal human beings, gender doesn't disqualify anyone's experience or perceptions. We bring our full abilities, recognizing that the skills that reside in each of us need to be developed for our common good.

We value consensus and action, knowing that as individuals, groups, and organizations, we all need to achieve our individual and collective purpose. Talking is said to be a woman's thing, and the idea of a "man of action" is a cliché. In a holistic world where the emphasis is on the whole, a consensus is forged before we act. Once we reach an agreement, we also move forward.

We share all of life, rejecting the idea that an individual's public vulnerability tarnishes their career. Many leaders shield others' view of their challenges, and most are considered fortunate if a close friend or two is aware of their "stuff." Men and women leaders alike are reluctant to share; consequently, the challenges, isolation, sense of no one understanding, and feelings of being different grow in darkness. Let's create professional settings where sharing isn't the undoing of any leader or team member; rather, a reservoir of strength. It was after my nearly being fired from my job and my lack of sharing when I had COVID that I learned to refill my reservoir. Sharing builds strength, it does not take it away. We recognize our limits and our need for others. No one person has all the answers. It may be difficult to say, "I don't know" or "I need more research." Consider leading with the words, "Here's what I know so far..." That's the best any of us can do.

We collaborate because we're convinced that partnership is how significant accomplishments get done. It doesn't matter whether you're a girl or boy or gender fluid when you have colleagues willing to dance together. We cleanse together, knowing and accepting that shame, blame, and hurt must come out. Sometimes sharing helps reveal the real issues. Or it comes through crying. Or screaming. We let it rise from the depths of our being. When it comes out and we listen to it, cleansing happens. Health and love have a chance to grow.

We transition from fear together, knowing that what we call fear is a sign that we've lost our connection to our core essence and consequently each other. This is where we make our stand. I am part of a larger whole where everyone is equal. Each person in this "whole" is a unique individual. We may have different responsibilities and perform other functions, yet we are one. We are a community. This is how one part of the whole becomes part of the We.

This is the kind of work environment we strive towards. Can you envision this workplace? A place that embodies these principles? Would you feel confident engaging in a team in this environment? Our accomplishments could be unbelievable.

There is a survival instinct that researchers have observed in the eruption of primal self-preservation, which includes fighting and a lack of social preservation. Yes, the most elementary human instinct is survival. Our real drive is survival through connectedness to community. We are born with this instinct that in the past has exhibited itself through conquest and control of food, land, power, and more. This drive to survive could be about staying in the community. Bonding together.

We are growing strong as whole human beings. Instead of creating a bigger wall, build a bigger table.

Come together. Thrive.

TAKE THE TIME TO QUESTION

As leaders, we exist in all kinds of relationships driven by urgency. As we interact with others, we likely rank timeliness and expedience among our top priorities. We want something worded differently. We voice our desire for quick improvement. We drive budgets, schedules, and complex issues with a fierceness that can often be over the top. Getting things done with a gentle touch means considering when and how we talk with others. Our timing might not be theirs. And the way we broach a subject can be considerate, or it can be brutal. The outcome can often match the approach.

Sometimes I will start a conversation by clearing the way. "Mary," I'll say, "You have been tired lately, and I know that you're not on top of things."

What a terrible way to start. I immediately put her on the defensive, denying her a fresh way of responding. She inevitably will react rather than respond.

I have learned that starting with a question instead of a statement can do wonders. "How are you, Mary? I loved the energy that was created from your last presentation. Where did you get those fabulous examples?"

This sounds simple, and yet it hasn't always been simple for me, and knowing this helps me realize it's also not easy for others.

Part of our reluctance as leaders to share our own needs, professional or personal, is that we are reluctant to add anything to the work conversation that might feed negativity. Inadvertently, however, we might further a culture of toxic positivity where brutal realities remain unaddressed, and relationships break down. If we are perpetually positive, it can be toxic to an individual or an organization because it doesn't leave space for hard stuff to come out. Toxic positivity is dysfunctional. It is an ineffective over-the-top injection of optimistic happiness imposed onto all situations. This results in denial and lacks true human validation. It can harm people who are going through difficult times.

Instead of this toxicity, we can alter our communication to acknowledge pain, stress, anxiety, and of course, the positive goodness. People will continue to be hurt if we don't address what that hurt entails. We've got to listen. Once we become more aware of people's deeper wounds, the more extraordinary gifts of a genuine relationship emerge. This happens both at work and at home.

When I spoke about refilling my reservoir by sharing my difficulties, this came about by putting my humility on the table and accepting the encouragement and help of others.

We are often pressured, in academia, to set forth a perfect image, especially in leadership roles. We all face struggles and if we push them under the table, they will only fester. We need to create an atmosphere for both the faculty and the students that "nurses" individual feelings, recognizes their concerns and creates an environment where everyone feels comfortable sharing their struggles. We need to be there for support. Sometimes we feel we need to hide our inadequacies in order to keep our credibility. This is a huge mistake. In both personal and professional relationships, we will stop sharing and asking for support if we don't get validation. Positivity is important. Bottling up our emotions negatively impacts our well-being.

When I wrote about our aggressive, forward plan during Covid, I wasn't saying "everything is fine". It wasn't. Looking at the situation, dealing with the problems and coming up with solutions is a positive agenda. Ignoring and shaming creates stress and makes the problem worse. This is a form of gaslighting, which is the word we use when someone causes you to question your own sense of reality.

We need to constantly remind ourselves that this sharing will continue to bring strength and our credibility will not dive; it will soar.

LEAVINGS

I talk a lot about the joy of dancing with people; a much less comfortable subject is dancing around something. When I get a spontaneous call from someone asking me for a meeting right away, my heart immediately sinks. I think that they will be leaving. And if we don't get together, if the meeting is postponed or never materializes, that's when the dancing around begins. One of us is trying to hold off the inevitability of the departure news. When someone decides to leave our institution, the only aspect that I have control over is how I respond.

Early in my nursing career I experienced a lot of dancing around a situation. As a student, I flunked bed making four times. At that point in hospital history, making a bed was not that simple. We had rubber sheets, topped with another sheet that had to be folded on to the bed just right. We have all heard of hospital corners—not my forte. As a child I was able to disappear. I was a slider. I'd slip out of the house and hang with the cows. I never made a bed. So my fellow classmates thought I was a loser. It wasn't until catheters and more technical learning came into play that I blossomed. Nursing is a serious profession and I took it seriously. I succumbed and along with the things I valued most, I learned to make a bed. I also learned to dance with a problem rather than around it.

I was an RN when a two-year-old patient named Michael was admitted. He had been running through his house with complete abandonment when he fell through a window and landed two stories below on cement. ICUs were new at this time and Michael was admitted. He was in a vegetative state. Machines were keeping him alive. His head had taken the brunt of the fall and we, in the unit, knew he was not going to make it. His mom had a good life and they were happily content with their family when she became pregnant with Michael. She wasn't trying for another child, and yet their loving welcoming nature welcomed this new member of their family. They had Michael and of course rejoiced in their love for him. And then this happened. The guilt this mother felt was overwhelming. She told me that she hadn't anticipated another child and now she was paying the price.

This was a catholic hospital and at this time in history, the 1970s, there was not an option to go off life support. I was the only protestant on the staff and they asked me if I would "pull the plug." I did, and Michael died. I had the choice in how to respond. I knew the inevitability of the situation. I knew that I could end this trauma. I knew that Michael was no longer with us. Michael would be leaving us.

This experience reminded me of the inevitability of change. People die. Children have accidents. Life changes.

In our school, we don't believe in replacing people; however, we fill positions. Every person who joins our school community is a unique individual and an addition to our team. They become part of the fabric of our school community forever. If they choose to leave, their contribution and impact will always be in the school. We will always be different because they were here.

Our approach is very different from those with the approach "everyone is replaceable." Not here. Every person has an impact.

We don't replace people. We fill positions. We change the dance partner and maybe even learn a few new steps.

When a person leaves, I think about all I've done to support and grow this person. I worked at engaging every mechanism and pathway possible for their growth and the growth of our school. We financed their development. Opened the door to meaningful cross-training. Provided people with support to make that happen. I've already looked to future opportunities for that person.

In higher education, we're fortunate to work with many people for decades, yet there are always those who come and go. Why this person, and why now? Despite my logical mind working hard, I still have that sense of what did I miss? We enjoyed years of closeness. We could talk about anything. I assumed their space was in our future, and now they are leaving. The decision has been made and rarely does that change.

Some individuals in our setting find the complex mix of teaching, research, funding, and family needs too much. This requires a move. I've met incredible tenured faculty who chose to leave because they couldn't fully advance their potential. When they tell me they don't want to go, I know it's true. They'd like to stay and they know in their gut that they must leave to achieve their next goal.

When a team member announces their intention to leave, I don't try to change their mind. When they say they've been offered more money, I respond that we all receive offers. I don't negotiate. They know that I have given them all I can based on their experience and equity with their colleagues. And then I ask them, "Where is your heart?" I can't answer that for them.

And when they've made the decision, I coach them on leaving well. This is important as they continue their professional trajectory. I ask them to consider being transparent with the new person they call "the boss." I suggest they trust and make the most of that relationship. Ultimately, I do everything I can not to contribute to shame or guilt. I thank them for letting me know and that I'm always here if they need something. "You are always a member of this family," I say. "You are part of this woven tapestry." I wish them well in their private and public life.

When my husband left me and our son, something inside me cracked. That night I called a very wise friend and explained the situation. He said to me, "From this moment forward, you'll never be the same." This was a hard declaration to hear. Accepting this helped me welcome a new reality.

Leaving can be so significant that we need time for reflection. Not burying ourselves in our work, yet stepping back and going inside to absorb what's transpired and let it all settle in. There are so many tales of quiet quitting and finding one's work-life balance. Quitting is not a disease. Leaving is not an ending. It is a step in the direction we are heading in our lives. And hopefully, that direction is positive.

We know we are doing our part as leaders if we can embrace an ongoing, evolving relationship. Leavings don't cut us off from the whole; they leave a spot for some new growth. I ask them to come back and teach us what they've learned. I hope that we too can show them how we've continued because of their contributions, and no, we have not replaced them; we have filled the position. We continue to evolve.

Of course, the very biggest leaving is death. When that little boy, Michael, lay in my ICU unit, I knew that he was leaving. Permanently leaving. My choice, and need, to stop the life support system that kept his heart beating was not one I had studied. It was not a dance I had yet rehearsed. It was a compassionate decision to stop the machines that were supporting his life. It was a decision to let life end in a dignified way. It was ending the dance with a dignified final bow.

WORDS

If you're not in the medical or health field, you might have no idea what a doctor is talking about when she uses the words angiography, bilirubin, or cautery. Take a ride on a racing sailboat and listen as they talk about the baggywrinkle, the genoa, or the halyard. An orchestra conductor might stress that the beginning should be pianissimo, with the staccato coming at the end of the measure. And in business today, especially technology, the lingo changes daily. Our dictionaries are getting new words at a rate faster than most of us can keep up with. So what do all these words do to our communication?

We need language to share the experience. Every part of myself—my experiences, my background, and my education—all help shape my language. And language is one of the tools I use to lead. If I can't convey my ideas to others, then we will not accomplish our goals. We need clear language for productivity. The language I use needs to be in sync with my values.

My core values stay the same. They grow, the words change, and the focus shifts, yet the central values stay the same. My leadership revolves around my values. And I have learned that these need to be acted upon in my personal life, my relationships with friends and family, and in the relationships with my profession.

Words are important. To communicate well, we need to choose words that chart our purpose. They need to fit. Who is listening? Who is our audience? What are they wanting? Expecting? Needing? It takes thought and planning to get it right.

Practicing our values is where the work is. Professing through words makes them more accessible.

According to Pew Research, roughly a quarter of American adults say that they haven't read a book in the past year. Many people read texts, news spots, and Instagram posts and yet they don't read entire books. This alone will be a significant influence on language use. Society has trended towards the "fast food" way of reading, hearing information, and communicating. There is a saying that "just because everyone's doing it doesn't make it right." I have chosen silence over these "quick fixes" and person-to-person liaising rather than strings of daily texts. Words matter to me, and I choose them carefully when communicating with my team. It takes practice; I pause long enough to make sure that I speak from my own essence. What is it I really want to say? To whom am I speaking, and how will they hear what I have to say? I believe it's essential to choose one's words carefully so that an unhealthy ego doesn't come into play. I listen to what I say to ensure there's no judgment involved. I remind myself that I am building relationships, not disturbing or tearing them down. Sticks and stones may break your bones, and words really can hurt you. The old saying got it wrong.

Some of the examples I have:

- I don't talk about problem people or people having problems. We address challenges and opportunities.
- I won't use adversarial words.
- I won't use words that trigger anxiety, trauma or feelings of exclusion, or being othered.
- I avoid words that express entitlement or rank.

- I avoid "just," as it minimizes the point I'm trying to convey.
- I avoid the word "but,"' which invalidates whatever I've said.
- I don't ask people to admit or confess, which implies judgment. "Describe" is a more helpful word.
- I never say that I want to pick your brain. This phrase ignores a person's heart and implies I want to pry them open and take what I can without respect for the relationship.
- I do my utmost to reframe an opposing point of view into a positive one. What good can we notice, express gratitude for and expand on?

As I continue to communicate with others, these are the verbal watchouts that have emerged. As you listen carefully to others, you can develop your own list, realizing that even offhand comments can have a considerable good or destructive impact. The smallest of words can shut down a conversation. The correct word can open a powerful flow—can create that atmosphere of one which I so heartily seek.

When addressing colleagues, I am not trying to always be creative. I strive for consistency. In a report on the School of Nursing, I always start with my usual refrain: "The school is vibrant and innovative and in full partnership." I don't apologize for saying the same thing over and over. Being consistent risks being boring. However, there is a reassurance with predictability. As I engage with individuals, I begin with the certainty that their day has been full. So has mine. We are all swirling, or one might say, flowing. As a leader, I need to focus my attention on what we need to accomplish. A river flows, a conversation flows, and our school's mission can never be reached without the flow that comes from good communication.

Communication defines how I convey information, how I receive it, and how I use language to impart the message and also the feelings surrounding that piece of information. Words have such

power. And power has responsibility.
We need to heed the words we use. To use them wisely and for the benefit of all.

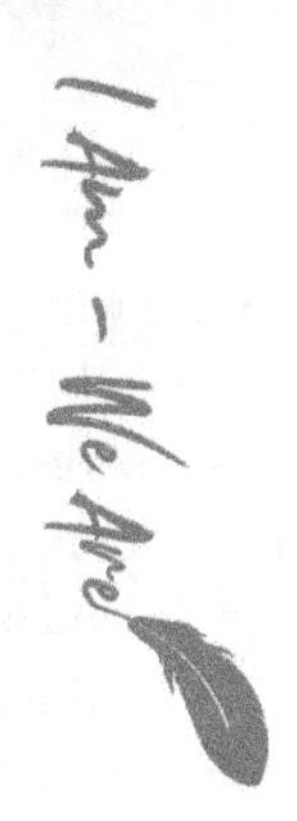

CO-CREATING

Adapt or fail. Remember Toys "R" Us? They went bankrupt. How about the video stores we used to peruse before selecting a movie and taking one home for our evening entertainment? Not around anymore. Did you ever have a BlackBerry? How about a Polaroid camera? These are all big names and big businesses that crashed. Was it a failure to adapt? There are many reasons. Not changing with the times is a big part of failing businesses.

And then there are those things that seemed normal and we eventually learned were not necessarily good. Lead was put into gasoline, and it was also a component of paint. We found how damaging lead is to our health, and these companies got rid of the lead. Hair spray and deodorant had chlorofluorocarbons that contributed to the destruction of the ozone layer. We got rid of that as well. I'm sure there are entire books written about changes that were both forced and needed.

COVID gave us a giant test of how well we can cope. We had to make changes when facing uncertainty. We were in a crisis that challenged us like most had never before experienced. Emergency teams were on high alert. The medical system was overloaded, yet we received great affirmation from the public, and with the help of many, we pushed through. If there's ever a "better than ever" time to lead with love, it's during a crisis.

When a challenge like COVID subsides, we have to readjust. With this experience and new knowledge, we create a new emphasis on prevention, sustainability, and even-deeper relationships that we can depend on.

Life is full of surprises and the onset of COVID forced significant innovation. We learned to value the interconnectedness that makes us one. This was not something that was happening to someone "over there." This was happening to all of us, and it was all of us acting together that got us through.

In higher education, we reached ICU levels of need. We at the School of Nursing were well prepared for the transformations forced by COVID. All our courses already had an online presence. We were flexible. We pride ourselves in being ready and are humbled by our good fortune. Many will not make it.

The healthcare system is broken. The pandemic exposed flaws and grave dysfunctionality in the system. Short- and long-term problems remain unaddressed:

- For more than a century, the United States has built a healthcare system focused on illness rather than health promotion and prevention. It's an approach dominated by pharma and other solutions prioritizing making money over wellbeing.
- Healthcare is unavailable to millions of people in the United States. Especially vulnerable are the homeless, children, the elderly, people of color, and anyone lacking private insurance. Highly deductible insurance plans prevent even many of the insured from accessing necessary care.
- Public health has been gutted, including the essential health services once freely provided to children at school. The degradation of public health over the past 40 years continues despite a massive influx of funding during COVID. As the

pandemic wanes, so does the common social purpose and investment.

- Despite the clear connection between dental care and cardiac disease, dentistry maintains a cartel status outside health insurance coverage. In most modern countries, dental care is health care.
- The financing of our healthcare system is unconscionable. We must seat healthcare professionals in partnership with hospital administrators to put care at the forefront. While we must be concerned about financial sustainability, people suffer when money is the priority.

These issues have plagued healthcare for decades. The time is gone for putting on patches rather than boldly transforming healthcare and devising lasting solutions. The time has come to learn lessons that many countries spending a fraction of the money to support health have learned.

Recent studies of the brain conclude that some people must go through all of the instructions, preparations, and directions before they try something. With something like open-heart surgery, this is a good idea. In learning big ideas, making changes, and adapting to a bigger world, the other kind of brain works better. This kind of brain dives right in. It doesn't wait to be asked or to be completely ready, or to have no fear. It gets on with it. And I believe that it is this kind of brain that we need to change our system.

We don't need someone to apply a patch. We need transformation. We need lasting solutions.

Throughout my career, I have known what many other nurses also know. Despite untold billions invested in healthcare, more straightforward solutions to supporting health promotion and illness prevention are ignored, and preventable mistakes continue to happen. Even where healthcare has seen progress, it has cost tens of billions of dollars to decrease the error rate by a single percentage point.

We have seen patient after patient contract systemic infections and die from being in the system. Worldwide, we have providers giving drugs that escalate the problem. Now, as an alternative to drugs, healthcare's next-generation solution involves helping people grow their own cells to fight against an issue. This looks enticing; however, we still do not know the long-term impact. Have we studied the ultimate outcome? Can we continue altering individuals' genetic makeup without permanently altering humanity? The questions are tough, and the answers are even more difficult.

We do have to move forward. Old formulas can't solve new problems. They've been tried. As leaders and team members, we are called to be on the edge of innovation. We cannot stay shopping in the video store when someone's life is on the line, when humanity is shaking. It's not a tweak that we need. It's a transformation.

Regarding our own nursing school's methodology for transformation, it takes work to define. It's less about the process than the synchronicity of the whole. Working together, we almost always come up with solutions. Transformation happens when we quit our denial and dive in. It's an immersion into the challenge that moves us forward.

We do not stay in our heads. That is not where the action is. We have the courage to move beyond self, to the WE ARE.

Nurses were some of the first healthcare professionals to see the potential of technology to improve patient care. It was in the eighties and nineties that nursing informatics really pushed forward as a discipline. Electronic health records were a major turning point and allowed nurses to share patient data more succinctly. Improvements were made in coordinating care and safety. This was a time when nurses made more informed, data-based decisions about patient care. Informatics was a major reason for my move from direct patient nursing to becoming a dean in the nursing school. I felt that it was vital to the future of healthcare and nursing practices and wanted to share this knowledge and expertise. Nurses with informatics expertise will be essential to the future of healthcare. Along with big data and artificial intelligence, we will be able to implement solutions to some of our biggest challenges.

We are focusing on broadening the circle beyond ourselves. In the time of COVID, many institutions were contracting and getting by. We went the other way. We entered several new international partnerships, including Hanoi Medical University and Powell College of Brazil. We signed new collaborative agreements in our home state so now have eight bold transformative entities. In the past, expanding these would have been considered a crazy move with a competitor. That is thinking from a duality standpoint. In a nondual world, it's called collaboration. Our new partnerships between the University of Minnesota, healthcare centers and universities in other parts of the world and fellow services in Minnesota will create a strong cooperation of clinical innovation and training. I am so proud of this. We are determined to move beyond the competition. We are building partnerships because we need each other.

The School of Nursing is determined to engage in partnership and collaboration, not activities where patients pay the price. We need to step out of that competitive cycle. We are also focused on partnering to discuss and resolve the nursing shortage, unlike anything we've seen for decades.

Besides the support we have within our school, we are very fortunate to have the support of the governing regents of our university. They recognize the dire crisis we are in. Even if we achieve full collaboration between all of Minnesota's healthcare entities, we will still face enormous challenges in meeting our state's healthcare needs, particularly the nursing workforce shortage.

Change doesn't sit next to us comfortably. It shows its head way out there. We have to stand up tall and look for it. We can become disillusioned. We can become despondent. We can become desperate. We cannot give up. Sometimes we have to work on the edge. We are respecting the system, acknowledging the system, and taking leaps out of it. Transformation does not usually happen in comfort. It happens on the edge. And when it happens, it raises grassroots energy. It creates opportunities. It flows into something bigger and better, and ... we don't even know what else.

I am running out of time. We all are. The world is in crisis, and I can sit in my comfortable seat, or I can keep working.

I have a level of wisdom that I want to give. I want to be part of the wheel. Leaders don't quit.

AWAKENING

Cesar Chavez said, "An organizer's job is to help ordinary people do extraordinary things."

I am the dean of the University of Minnesota School of Nursing. I am a leader. I am an organizer. I want to help realize great nurses. I want these nurses to be part of a greater whole: a world that looks after everyone. A world that concentrates on the We instead of the me. I want extraordinary things to happen.

It turns out that life gets in the way. The Chronicle of Higher Education conducted a survey about the high school graduating class of 2021. The theme was, "exhausted but optimistic." The authors expressed concerns about COVID, including health and safety, the ability to socialize, and future opportunities. The mental and emotional exhaustion felt by these students was high. Yet more than half of the survey subjects were eager to learn in person, and about half were optimistic about college. In the same issue of this Chronicle was an article titled The Great Disillusionment. The tagline is "College workers are burning out when they'll be needed most."

So what does that mean? Are we optimistic? Are we burnt out? Are we needy and depressed and lost?

Even in the years before COVID, teachers saw students having difficulty integrating into the school environment. Many needed one-to-one connection to get them on track. Addiction to technology was reducing students' ability to concentrate. It was dampening their consciousness. Experts report that more than seventy percent of students arriving at college need assistance to deal with documented anxiety or other mental health struggles.

We can't ignore this and hope it will go away. These are problems in today's society, and yet I believe that the untapped gifts these young people have are what we so desperately need. Our survivability as human beings depend on them. They are our future. I want them to find their place and succeed.

As leaders, we have an important job. We're here to contribute to the community; toward the healing and transformation of all humankind. That sounds huge. And yet that's one of the things we've gotten hung up on. Pay instead of a better way. Our destiny is far more than producing graduates or realizing revenue. We are positioned to walk alongside people struggling. We need to love them into a living that's inspiring. Our sought-after outcome is for all.

I believe in synchronicity. No encounter is an accident. We are each here for something we may or may not be able to articulate. When we are awakened, there is no limit, and what we perceive as problems become challenges. Difficulties become opportunities.

Will we answer this call? Will we put our efforts into what matters most? It's so easy to get bogged down. The daily grind can grind us into something small and inconsequential. Many of us keep our heads down. Whether in higher education, healthcare, or society, are we measuring our growth and success by the right metrics? We busy ourselves with priorities imposed on us and repeated without discernment. Are we conscious of what is genuinely vital? Let's keep asking questions. What is your purpose as a human being? How do you lead from that core? Do I put my ego aside?

Do I constantly put a greater purpose in my vision?

I can ask myself these questions, and I suggest you ask them yourself. What I can't do is teach people "awakening." We can help them discover who they are; alone they must do the digging. When people come to the School of Nursing as students, faculty, or staff, I understand that they need to live in a functioning world. They need a productive job and an income and benefits. I also hope that they want to be of service. That they are interested in the health of people. That they have a reason to be here that goes beyond self. I'm lucky if I get to remind people of their purpose. It can sometimes be easy to forget.

As leaders, we have privilege. The privilege of watching people grow into what they are meant to be. Transformative leadership comes from having courage, willingness to take risks, and transparency to speak openly. It's daring to authentically call life's great question: Why are you here?

I was fortunate to discover early that I had a destiny. I was born knowing I was meant to be here. Many people come to that realization much later, some perhaps never. I believe that deep in their hearts, the knowledge is already there.

Sometimes I look back on that little girl growing up on the farm. I look at the setbacks I dealt with and also the opportunities with which I've been blessed. I look at the people who nursed me and the nursing career I was privileged to embark upon. I now look at the shortage of nurses we have in Minnesota and globally. And I want to be that quiet person who whispers into your ear: be a nurse. Be a nurse to your family and your friends and your neighbors. Be a nurse to your community and your workplace. Be a nurse to the world and remember to nurse yourself. Nursing is about care. We need more nurses. Professional nurses. People who are committed to the greater good. People who understand how to combine professionalism with love.

I read once that everyone has a circle of influence. If you live in a small village in a jungle, you may have a circle of influence of only a handful of people. Someone else has influence within their family, their neighborhood, and their workplace. Others who are in political life or in the public eye have huge circles. What they do or say influences many.

I have a circle of influence with students, staff, and faculty, with graduates, the places they go to work, the health system they work in, and the population who benefits.

Nursing is huge. And if I have that much influence and can lead with love, imagine what we can accomplish. One world. One caring, loving world. The connections are building. The fire's been lit. Transformation is inevitable. I hope you're willing to make the journey with me. We can do it if we do it together.

L.R. Knost wrote: "Do not be dismayed by the brokenness of the world. All things break. And all things can be mended. Not with time, as they say, but with intention. So go. Love intentionally, extravagantly, unconditionally. The broken world waits in darkness for the light that is you."

About the Author

Connie White Delaney, Ph.D., RN, FAAN, FACMI, FNAP

Transforming the Future through Love and AI

In an era shaped by rapid technological change, Connie White Delaney stands out as a leader who marries compassion with computational power. With her belief in leading with love, Delaney blends her expertise in building integrated communities, programs, and systems with the revolutionary capabilities of artificial intelligence (AI).

As Professor and Dean at the School of Minnesota's School of Nursing and Knowledge Generation Lead for the National Center for Interprofessional Practice and Education, Delaney knows that artificial intelligence needs to be utilized. She also believes in the importance of guiding this new intelligence by leading with love.

An internationally recognized thought leader, Delaney's contributions to the field are expansive, from serving as an Associate Director of the Clinical Translational Science Institute–Biomedical Informatics to acting as the Director of the Institute for Health Informatics (IHI) in the Academic Health Center. She received an Honorary Doctor of Philosophy in Nursing from the University of Iceland in 2011 and serves as an adjunct professor there, illustrating her global reach and influence.

Delaney is also a devoted researcher in data and IT standards for nursing, healthcare, and interprofessional practice and education. Her efforts extend to big data science and integrative informatics, aiming to bridge disciplinary divides and harness the power of information to effect positive change.

Delaney is past President of the Foundation of the National Institutes of Nursing Research (FNINR) and past Vice-Chair of CGFNS, Inc. Her educational background is as extensive as her professional accomplishments, spanning nursing and mathematics, educational administration, and computer applications, including postdoctoral study in nursing and medical informatics, and graduate study in integrative health and healing.

Connie White Delaney exemplifies the power of leading with love, infusing this ethos into her work at the crossroads of AI and transformative leadership. With her visionary approach and dedication to conscious well-being, Delaney is laying the groundwork for a future where love, technology, and human connection coalesce, forming the backbone of a brighter, more compassionate flourishing world.

If you want to text Connie's digital twin, register on the website to get access:
https://conniedelaney.com

Printed in the USA
CPSIA information can be obtained
at www.ICGtesting.com
LVHW011353280124
769813LV00069B/2115